Set
A

KEY STAGE 3
Levels 4–7

Shakespeare
Test Paper

English

The Tempest

Shakespeare Test Paper

CW00693772

The Tempest

Instructions:

- find a quiet place where you can sit down and complete the test paper undisturbed

- make sure you have all the necessary equipment to complete the test paper

- read the question carefully

- answer the question on lined paper

- go through and check your answer when you have finished writing

Time:

This test paper is **45 minutes** long.

You are being tested on your reading and understanding of the Shakespeare scenes you have studied.

Check how you have done against the mark scheme in the Instructions, Answers and Mark Scheme Booklet.

	Max. Mark	**Actual Mark**
Score	18	....

First name ....

Last name ....

The Tempest

You should spend about 45 minutes on this section.

The Tempest

In these scenes, we see Prospero dealing with Ferdinand and Miranda.

What do we learn about Prospero in these scenes?

Support your ideas by referring to both of the extracts which are printed on the following pages.

(18 marks)

Use the printed scenes to answer the question set on page 3.

Act 1 Scene 2

PROSPERO   *(To MIRANDA)* The fringèd curtains of thine eye advance,
And say what thou see'st yond.

MIRANDA   What is't? A spirit?
Lord, how it looks about! Believe me, sir,
It carries a brave form. But 'tis a spirit.   415

PROSPERO   No, wench: it eats and sleeps and hath such senses
As we have, such. This gallant which thou see'st
Was in the wreck – and, but he's something stained
With grief (that's beauty's canker), thou might'st call him
A goodly person. He hath lost his fellows,   420
And strays about to find 'em.

MIRANDA   I might call him
A thing divine, for nothing natural
I ever saw so noble.

PROSPERO   *(Aside)* It goes on, I see,
As my soul prompts it. *(To Ariel)* Spirit, fine spirit! I'll
    free thee
Within two days for this.

FERDINAND   *(Seeing MIRANDA)*   Most sure the goddess   425
On whom these airs attend! Vouchsafe my prayer
May know if you remain upon this island –
And that you will some good instruction give
How I may bear me here. My prime request,
Which I do last pronounce, is – O, you wonder! –   430
If you be maid or no?

MIRANDA   No wonder, sir;
But certainly a maid.

FERDINAND   My language! Heavens!
I am the best of them that speak this speech,
Were I but where 'tis spoken.

PROSPERO   How, the best?
What wert thou, if the King of Naples heard thee?   435

FERDINAND	A single thing, as I am now, that wonders
	To hear thee speak of Naples. He does hear me –
	And that he does I weep. Myself am Naples,
	Who with mine eyes, ne'er since at ebb, beheld
	The King my father wrecked.

| MIRANDA | Alack, for mercy! | 440 |

| FERDINAND | Yes, faith, and all his lords – the Duke of Milan |
| | And his brave son being twain. |

PROSPERO	(Aside) The Duke of Milan
	And his more braver daughter could control thee,
	If now 'twere fit to do't. At the first sight
	They have changed eyes. Delicate Ariel,	445
	I'll set thee free for this. (To FERDINAND) A word, good
	sir.
	I fear you have done yourself some wrong. A word.

MIRANDA	(Aside) Why speaks my father so ungently? This
	Is the third man that e'er I saw – the first
	That e'er I sighed for. Pity move my father	450
	To be inclined my way!

FERDINAND	O, if a virgin,
	And your affection not gone forth, I'll make you
	The Queen of Naples!

PROSPERO	Soft, sir! One word more.
	(Aside) They are both in either's powers. But this swift
	business
	I must uneasy make, lest too light winning	455
	Make the prize light. (To FERDINAND) One word more:
	I charge thee
	That thou attend me. Thou dost here usurp
	The name thou ow'st not – and hast put thyself
	Upon this island as a spy, to win it
	From me, the lord on't.

| FERDINAND | No, as I am a man! | 460 |

MIRANDA	There's nothing ill can dwell in such a temple.
	If the ill spirit have so fair a house,
	Good things will strive to dwell with't.

Turn over

PROSPERO	*(To FERDINAND)* Follow me!
	(To MIRANDA) Speak not you for him; he's a traitor. *(To FERDINAND)* Come!
	I'll manacle thy neck and feet together. 465
	Sea-water shalt thou drink: thy food shall be
	The fresh-brook mussels, withered roots, and husks
	Wherein the acorn cradled. Follow!

Act 3 Scene 1

MIRANDA	Do you love me?
FERDINAND	O heaven, O earth, bear witness to this sound
	And crown what I profess with kind event,
	If I speak true! If hollowly, invert 70
	What best is boded me to mischief! I,
	Beyond all limit of what else i'the world,
	Do love, prize, honour you.
MIRANDA	I am a fool
	To weep at what I am glad of.
PROSPERO	*(Aside)* Fair encounter
	Of two most rare affections! Heavens rain grace 75
	On that which breeds between 'em!
FERDINAND	Wherefore weep you?
MIRANDA	At mine unworthiness, that dare not offer
	What I desire to give; and much less take
	What I shall die to want. But this is trifling –
	And all the more it seeks to hide itself, 80
	The bigger bulk it shows. Hence, bashful cunning!
	And prompt me, plain and holy innocence!
	I am your wife if you will marry me:
	If not, I'll die your maid. To be your fellow
	You may deny me; but I'll be your servant, 85
	Whether you will or no.
FERDINAND	My mistress, dearest,
	(He kneels) And I thus humble ever.
MIRANDA	My husband, then?
FERDINAND	Ay, with a heart as willing
	As bondage e'er of freedom! Here's my hand.

MIRANDA	And mine, with my heart in't. And now farewell	90
	Till half an hour hence.	

FERDINAND	A thousand thousand!

Exit MIRANDA. Exit FERDINAND, separately, carrying the log.

PROSPERO	So glad of this as they I cannot be,	
	Who are surprised with all – but my rejoicing	
	At nothing can be more. I'll to my book –	
	For yet, ere supper time, must I perform	95
	Much business appertaining.	

Exit.

END OF TEST

Set **A**

KEY STAGE 3
Levels 4–7

Shakespeare
Test Paper

English

Romeo and Juliet

Shakespeare Test Paper

Romeo and Juliet

Instructions:

- find a quiet place where you can sit down and complete the test paper undisturbed

- make sure you have all the necessary equipment to complete the test paper

- read the question carefully

- answer the question on lined paper

- go through and check your answer when you have finished writing

Time:

This test paper is **45 minutes** long.

You are being tested on your reading and understanding of the Shakespeare scenes you have studied.

Check how you have done against the mark scheme in the Instructions, Answers and Mark Scheme Booklet.

	Max. Mark	**Actual Mark**
Score	18	....

First name ....

Last name ....

Romeo and Juliet

You should spend about 45 minutes on this section.

Romeo and Juliet

In these scenes, the audience see Romeo in different situations.

What do we learn about Romeo in these two scenes?

Support your ideas by referring to both of the extracts which are printed on the following pages.

(18 marks)

Act 1 Scene 1

| ROMEO | Ay me, sad hours seem long. | 155 |
| | Was that my father that went hence so fast? | |

| BENVOLIO | It was. What sadness lengthens Romeo's hours? | |

| ROMEO | Not having that which, having, makes them short. | |

| BENVOLIO | In love? | |

| ROMEO | Out – | 160 |

| BENVOLIO | Of love? | |

| ROMEO | Out of her favour where I am in love. | |

| BENVOLIO | Alas, that Love, so gentle in his view, | |
| | Should be so tyrannous and rough in proof! | |

ROMEO	Alas, that Love, whose view is muffled still,	165
	Should without eyes see pathways to his will!	
	Where shall we dine? O me! What fray was here?	
	Yet tell me not, for I have heard it all.	
	Here's much to do with hate, but more with love.	
	Why then, O brawling love, O loving hate,	170
	O anything of nothing first create!	
	O heavy lightness, serious vanity,	
	Misshapen chaos of well-seeming forms!	
	Feather of lead, bright smoke, cold fire, sick health,	
	Still-waking sleep, that is not what it is!	175
	This love feel I, that feel no love in this.	
	Dost thou not laugh?	

| BENVOLIO | No, coz, I rather weep. | |

| ROMEO | Good heart, at what? | |

| BENVOLIO | At *thy* good heart's oppression. | |

ROMEO	Why, such is love's transgression.	
	Griefs of mine own lie heavy in my breast,	180
	Which thou wilt propagate to have it pressed	
	With more of thine. This love that thou hast shown	
	Doth add more grief to too much of mine own.	

Love is a smoke made with the fume of sighs:
Being purged, a fire sparkling in lovers' eyes;   185
Being vexed, a sea nourished with loving tears.
What is it else? A madness most discreet,
A choking gall, and a preserving sweet.
Farewell, my coz.

BENVOLIO   Soft, I will go along –
And if you leave me so, you do me wrong.   190

ROMEO   Tut, I have lost myself. I am not here.
This is not Romeo: he's some other where.

BENVOLIO   Tell me in sadness, who is that you love?

ROMEO   What, shall I groan and tell thee?

BENVOLIO   Groan? Why no –
But sadly tell me who.   195

ROMEO   Bid a sick man in sadness make his will –
A word ill urged to one that is so ill.
In sadness, cousin, I do love a woman.

BENVOLIO   I aimed so near when I supposed you loved.

ROMEO   A right good mark-man! And she's fair I love.   200

BENVOLIO   A right fair mark, fair coz, is soonest hit.

ROMEO   Well, in that hit you miss. She'll not be hit
With Cupid's arrow. She hath Dian's wit,
And in strong proof of chastity well-armed,
From Love's weak childish bow she lives uncharmed.   205
She will not stay the siege of loving terms,
Nor bide th' encounter of assailing eyes,
Nor ope her lap to saint-seducing gold.
O, she is rich in beauty – only poor
That when she dies, with beauty dies her store.   210

BENVOLIO   Then she hath sworn that she will still live chaste?

ROMEO   She hath, and in that sparing makes huge waste,
For beauty, starved with her severity,
Cuts beauty off from all posterity.
She is too fair, too wise, wisely too fair,   215
To merit bliss by making me despair.
She hath forsworn to love, and in that vow
Do I live dead, that live to tell it now.

Turn over

BENVOLIO	Be ruled by me: forget to think of her.	
ROMEO	O, teach me how I should forget to think!	220
BENVOLIO	By giving liberty unto thine eyes: Examine other beauties.	

ROMEO

                              'Tis the way
To call hers – exquisite – in question more.
These happy masks that kiss fair ladies' brows,
Being black, puts us in mind they hide the fair.   225
He that is strucken blind cannot forget
The precious treasure of his eyesight lost.
Show me a mistress that is passing fair:
What doth her beauty serve, but as a note
Where I may read who passed that passing fair?   230
Farewell. Thou canst not teach me to forget.

BENVOLIO   I'll pay that doctrine, or else die in debt.

Exeunt.

Act 2 Scene 2

The garden, beside the Capulet house.
ROMEO comes forward (reacting to MERCUTIO's joking).

ROMEO   He jests at scars that never felt a wound.

Enter JULIET, coming to her window-balcony above.
ROMEO, below, sees the light at the window, then realises it is JULIET.

– But soft! What light through yonder window breaks?
It is the east, and Juliet is the sun.
Arise, fair sun, and kill the envious moon,
Who is already sick and pale with grief   5
That thou her maid art far more fair than she.
Be not her maid, since she is envious:
Her vestal livery is but sick and green,
And none but fools do wear it. Cast it off.
– It is my lady! – O, it is my love!   10
O that she knew she were!
She speaks – yet she says nothing. What of that?
Her eye discourses. I will answer it.
– I am too bold. 'Tis not to me she speaks.
Two of the fairest stars in all the heaven,   15
Having some business, do entreat her eyes
To twinkle in their spheres till they return.

What if her eyes were there, they in her head?
The brightness of her cheek would shame those stars
As daylight doth a lamp. Her eyes in heaven 20
Would through the airy region stream so bright
That birds would sing and think it were not night!
See how she leans her cheek upon her hand.
O that I were a glove upon that hand,
That I might touch that cheek!

JULIET   Ay me!
ROMEO   *(Aside)* She speaks. 25
O speak again, bright angel! – For thou art
As glorious to this night, being o'er my head,
As is a wingèd messenger of heaven
Unto the white-upturnèd wondering eyes
Of mortals that fall back to gaze on him 30
When he bestrides the lazy-pacing clouds,
And sails upon the bosom of the air.

JULIET   O Romeo, Romeo! Wherefore art thou Romeo?
Deny thy father and refuse thy name –
Or if thou wilt not, be but sworn my love 35
And I'll no longer be a Capulet.

ROMEO   *(Aside)* Shall I hear more, or shall I speak at this?

JULIET   'Tis but thy name that is my enemy.
Thou art myself, though not a Montague.
What's 'Montague'? It is nor hand, nor foot, 40
Nor arm, nor face, nor any other part
Belonging to a man. O, be some other name!
What's in a name? That which we call a rose
By any other word would smell as sweet.
So Romeo would, were he not Romeo called, 45
Retain that dear perfection which he owes
Without that title. Romeo, doff thy name –
And for that name, which is no part of thee,
Take all myself.

ROMEO   I take thee at thy word.
Call me but love, and I'll be new-baptized. 50
Henceforth, I never will be Romeo.

END OF TEST

Set **C**

KEY STAGE 3
Levels 4–7

Shakespeare
Test Paper

English

Shakespeare Test Paper

The Tempest

Instructions:

- find a quiet place where you can sit down and complete the test paper undisturbed

- make sure you have all the necessary equipment to complete the test paper

- read the question carefully

- answer the question on lined paper

- go through and check your answer when you have finished writing

Time:

This test paper is **45 minutes** long.

You are being tested on your reading and understanding of the Shakespeare scenes you have studied.

Check how you have done against the mark scheme in the Instructions, Answers and Mark Scheme Booklet.

	Max. Mark	**Actual Mark**
Score	18	....

First name   ....

Last name   ....

The Tempest

You should spend about 45 minutes on this section.

The Tempest

In these scenes, we see Ferdinand falling in love with Miranda.

What do we learn about Ferdinand in these scenes?

Support your ideas by referring to both of the extracts which are printed on the following pages.

(18 marks)

Use the printed scenes to answer the question set on page 3.

Act 1 Scene 2

FERDINAND	The ditty does remember my drowned father.	
	This is no mortal business, nor no sound	410
	That the earth owes. I hear it now above me.	

PROSPERO
(To MIRANDA) The fringèd curtains of thine eye advance,
And say what thou see'st yond.

MIRANDA
What is't? A spirit?
Lord, how it looks about! Believe me, sir,
It carries a brave form. But 'tis a spirit. 415

PROSPERO
No, wench: it eats and sleeps and hath such senses
As we have, such. This gallant which thou see'st
Was in the wreck – and, but he's something stained
With grief (that's beauty's canker), thou might'st call him
A goodly person. He hath lost his fellows, 420
And strays about to find 'em.

MIRANDA
I might call him
A thing divine, for nothing natural
I ever saw so noble.

PROSPERO
(Aside) It goes on, I see,
As my soul prompts it. *(To ARIEL)* Spirit, fine spirit! I'll
    free thee
Within two days for this.

FERDINAND
(Seeing MIRANDA) Most sure the goddess 425
On whom these airs attend! Vouchsafe my prayer
May know if you remain upon this island –
And that you will some good instruction give
How I may bear me here. My prime request,
Which I do last pronounce, is – O, you wonder! – 430
If you be maid or no?

MIRANDA
No wonder, sir;
But certainly a maid.

FERDINAND
My language! Heavens!
I am the best of them that speak this speech,
Were I but where 'tis spoken.

PROSPERO	How, the best?	
	What wert thou, if the King of Naples heard thee?	435

FERDINAND	A single thing, as I am now, that wonders	
	To hear thee speak of Naples. He does hear me –	
	And that he does I weep. Myself am Naples,	
	Who with mine eyes, ne'er since at ebb, beheld	
	The King my father wrecked.	

MIRANDA	Alack, for mercy!	440

FERDINAND	Yes, faith, and all his lords – the Duke of Milan	
	And his brave son being twain.	

PROSPERO	*(Aside)* The Duke of Milan	
	And his more braver daughter could control thee,	
	If now 'twere fit to do't. At the first sight	
	They have changed eyes. Delicate Ariel,	445
	I'll set thee free for this. *(To FERDINAND)* A word, good	
	sir.	
	I fear you have done yourself some wrong. A word.	

MIRANDA	*(Aside)* Why speaks my father so ungently? This	
	Is the third man that e'er I saw – the first	
	That e'er I sighed for. Pity move my father	450
	To be inclined my way!	

FERDINAND	O, if a virgin,	
	And your affection not gone forth, I'll make you	
	The Queen of Naples!	

Turn over

Act 3 Scene 1

In front of PROSPERO's cave.
Enter FERDINAND, carrying a log.

FERDINAND   *(Putting down the log)* There be some sports are
           painful, and their labour
Delight in them sets off. Some kinds of baseness
Are nobly undergone, and most poor matters
Point to rich ends. This my mean task
Would be as heavy to me as odious, but   5
The mistress which I serve quickens what's dead,
And makes my labours pleasures. O, she is
Ten times more gentle than her father's crabbed –
And he's composed of harshness! I must remove
Some thousands of these logs, and pile them up,   10
Upon a sore injunction. My sweet mistress
Weeps when she sees me work, and says such baseness
Had never like executor. I forget –
(He picks up the log again)
– But these sweet thoughts do even refresh my labours,
Most busiest, when I do it.

Enter MIRANDA – and PROSPERO, who watches from a distance, unseen.

MIRANDA   Alas now, pray you   15
Work not so hard! I would the lightning had
Burnt up those logs that you are enjoined to pile!
Pray, set it down, and rest you. When this burns,
'Twill weep for having wearied you. My father
Is hard at study. Pray, now, rest yourself.   20
He's safe for these three hours.

FERDINAND   O most dear mistress,
The sun will set before I shall discharge
What I must strive to do.

MIRANDA   If you'll sit down.
I'll bear your logs the while. Pray give me that:
I'll carry it to the pile.

FERDINAND   No, precious creature.   25
I had rather crack my sinews, break my back,
Than you should such dishonour undergo,
While I sit lazy by.

MIRANDA	It would become me
	As well as it does you – and I should do it
	With much more ease, for my good will is to it,	30
	And yours it is against.

| PROSPERO | *(Aside)* Poor worm, thou art infected! |
| | This visitation shows it. |

| MIRANDA | You look wearily. |

FERDINAND	No, noble mistress. 'Tis fresh morning with me
	When you are by at night. I do beseech you –
	(Putting down the log) Chiefly that I might set it in my
	prayers –	35
	What is your name?

| MIRANDA | Miranda. O my father, |
| | I have broke your hest to say so! |

FERDINAND	Admired Miranda!
	Indeed the top of admiration – worth
	What's dearest to the world! Full many a lady
	I have eyed with best regard, and many a time	40
	The harmony of their tongues hath into bondage
	Brought my too diligent ear. For several virtues
	Have I liked several women – never any
	With so full soul, but some defect in her
	Did quarrel with the noblest grace she owed,	45
	And put it to the foil. But you – o you,
	So perfect and so peerless – are created
	Of every creature's best!

END OF TEST

Set
B

KEY STAGE 3
Levels 4–7

Shakespeare
Test Paper

English

Shakespeare Test Paper

The Tempest

The Tempest

Instructions:

- find a quiet place where you can sit down and complete the test paper undisturbed

- make sure you have all the necessary equipment to complete the test paper

- read the question carefully

- answer the question on lined paper

- go through and check your answer when you have finished writing

Time:

This test paper is **45 minutes** long.

You are being tested on your reading and understanding of the Shakespeare scenes you have studied.

Check how you have done against the mark scheme in the Instructions, Answers and Mark Scheme Booklet.

	Max. Mark	**Actual Mark**
Score	18	....

First name ....

Last name ....

The Tempest

You should spend about 45 minutes on this section.

The Tempest

In these scenes, we see Miranda's first dealings with Ferdinand.

What do we learn about Miranda in these scenes?

Support your ideas by referring to both of the extracts which are printed on the following pages.

(18 marks)

Act 1 Scene 2

PROSPERO   *(To MIRANDA)* The fringèd curtains of thine eye advance,
            And say what thou see'st yond.

MIRANDA   What is't? A spirit?
            Lord, how it looks about! Believe me, sir,
            It carries a brave form. But 'tis a spirit.   415

PROSPERO   No, wench: it eats and sleeps and hath such senses
            As we have, such. This gallant which thou see'st
            Was in the wreck – and, but he's something stained
            With grief (that's beauty's canker), thou might'st call him
            A goodly person. He hath lost his fellows,   420
            And strays about to find 'em.

MIRANDA   I might call him
            A thing divine, for nothing natural
            I ever saw so noble.

PROSPERO   *(Aside)* It goes on, I see,
            As my soul prompts it. *(To ARIEL)* Spirit, fine spirit! I'll
                free thee
            Within two days for this.

FERDINAND   *(Seeing MIRANDA)* Most sure the goddess   425
            On whom these airs attend! Vouchsafe my prayer
            May know if you remain upon this island –
            And that you will some good instruction give
            How I may bear me here. My prime request,
            Which I do last pronounce, is – O, you wonder! –   430
            If you be maid or no?

MIRANDA   No wonder, sir;
            But certainly a maid.

FERDINAND   My language! Heavens!
            I am the best of them that speak this speech,
            Were I but where 'tis spoken.

PROSPERO   How, the best?
            What wert thou, if the King of Naples heard thee?   435

FERDINAND   A single thing, as I am now, that wonders
            To hear thee speak of Naples. He does hear me –
            And that he does I weep. Myself am Naples,
            Who with mine eyes, ne'er since at ebb, beheld
            The King my father wrecked.

MIRANDA   Alack, for mercy!   440

FERDINAND   Yes, faith, and all his lords – the Duke of Milan
            And his brave son being twain.

PROSPERO   (Aside) The Duke of Milan
            And his more braver daughter could control thee,
            If now 'twere fit to do't. At the first sight
            They have changed eyes. Delicate Ariel,   445
            I'll set thee free for this. (To FERDINAND) A word, good
                sir.
            I fear you have done yourself some wrong. A word.

MIRANDA   (Aside) Why speaks my father so ungently? This
            Is the third man that e'er I saw – the first
            That e'er I sighed for. Pity move my father   450
            To be inclined my way!

FERDINAND   O, if a virgin,
            And your affection not gone forth, I'll make you
            The Queen of Naples!

PROSPERO   Soft, sir! One word more.
            (Aside) They are both in either's powers. But this swift
                business
            I must uneasy make, lest too light winning   455
            Make the prize light. (To FERDINAND) One word more:
                I charge thee
            That thou attend me. Thou dost here usurp
            The name thou ow'st not – and hast put thyself
            Upon this island as a spy, to win it
            From me, the lord on't.

FERDINAND   No, as I am a man!   460

MIRANDA   There's nothing ill can dwell in such a temple.
            If the ill spirit have so fair a house,
            Good things will strive to dwell with't.

Turn over

Act 3 Scene 1

Enter MIRANDA – and PROSPERO, who watches from a distance, unseen.

MIRANDA	Alas now, pray you	15

Work not so hard! I would the lightning had
Burnt up those logs that you are enjoined to pile!
Pray, set it down, and rest you. When this burns,
'Twill weep for having wearied you. My father
Is hard at study. Pray, now, rest yourself.   20
He's safe for these three hours.

FERDINAND   O most dear mistress,
The sun will set before I shall discharge
What I must strive to do.

MIRANDA   If you'll sit down.
I'll bear your logs the while. Pray give me that:
I'll carry it to the pile.

FERDINAND   No, precious creature.   25
I had rather crack my sinews, break my back,
Than you should such dishonour undergo,
While I sit lazy by.

MIRANDA   It would become me
As well as it does you – and I should do it
With much more ease, for my good will is to it,   30
And yours it is against.

PROSPERO   *(Aside)* Poor worm, thou art infected!
This visitation shows it.

MIRANDA   You look wearily.

FERDINAND No, noble mistress. 'Tis fresh morning with me
When you are by at night. I do beseech you –
(Putting down the log) Chiefly that I might set it in my prayers –   35
What is your name?

MIRANDA   Miranda. O my father,
I have broke your hest to say so!

FERDINAND   Admired Miranda!
Indeed the top of admiration – worth
What's dearest to the world! Full many a lady
I have eyed with best regard, and many a time   40
The harmony of their tongues hath into bondage

Brought my too diligent ear. For several virtues
Have I liked several women – never any
With so full soul, but some defect in her
Did quarrel with the noblest grace she owed,   45
And put it to the foil. But you – o you,
So perfect and so peerless – are created
Of every creature's best!

MIRANDA   I do not know
One of my sex – no woman's face remember,
Save, from my glass, mine own. Nor have I seen   50
More that I may call men than you, good friend,
And my dear father. How features are abroad,
I am skilless of – but, by my modesty,
The jewel in my dower, I would not wish
Any companion in the world but you –   55
Nor can imagination form a shape,
Besides yourself, to like of. But I prattle
Something too wildly, and my father's precepts
I therein do forget.

FERDINAND   I am, in my condition,
A prince, Miranda: I do think, a King –   60
I would not so! – and would no more endure
This wooden slavery than to suffer
The flesh-fly blow my mouth. Hear my soul speak:
The very instant that I saw you, did
My heart fly to your service – there resides,   65
To make me slave to it – and for your sake
Am I this patient log-man.

MIRANDA   Do you love me?

FERDINAND   O heaven, O earth, bear witness to this sound
And crown what I profess with kind event,
If I speak true! If hollowly, invert   70
What best is boded me to mischief! I,
Beyond all limit of what else i'the world,
Do love, prize, honour you.

MIRANDA   I am a fool
To weep at what I am glad of.

END OF TEST

Set

C

KEY STAGE 3
Levels 4–7

Shakespeare
Test Paper

English

Romeo and Juliet

Shakespeare Test Paper

Romeo and Juliet

Instructions:

- find a quiet place where you can sit down and complete the test paper undisturbed

- make sure you have all the necessary equipment to complete the test paper

- read the question carefully

- answer the question on lined paper

- go through and check your answer when you have finished writing

Time:

This test paper is **45 minutes** long.

You are being tested on your reading and understanding of the Shakespeare scenes you have studied.

Check how you have done against the mark scheme in the Instructions, Answers and Mark Scheme Booklet.

	Max. Mark	**Actual Mark**
Score	18	....

First name ....

Last name ....

Romeo and Juliet

You should spend about 45 minutes on this section.

Romeo and Juliet

In these scenes, other characters give their opinions on Romeo.

What do we learn about attitudes towards Romeo in these scenes?

Support your ideas by referring to both of the extracts which are printed on the following pages.

(18 marks)

Turn over

Act 1 Scene 1

LADY MONTAGUE	O where is Romeo? Saw you him today?	110
	Right glad I am he was not at this fray.	
BENVOLIO	Madam, an hour before the worshipped sun	
	Peered forth the golden window of the east,	
	A troubled mind drove me to walk abroad –	
	Where, underneath the grove of sycamore	115
	That westward rooteth from this city side,	
	So early walking did I see your son.	
	Towards him I made, but he was ware of me,	
	And stole into the covert of the wood.	
	I, measuring his affections by my own,	120
	Which then most sought where most might not be found,	
	Being one too many by my weary self,	
	Pursued my humour not pursuing his,	
	And gladly shunned who gladly fled from me.	
MONTAGUE	Many a morning hath he there been seen,	125
	With tears augmenting the fresh morning's dew,	
	Adding to clouds more clouds with his deep sighs.	
	But all so soon as the all-cheering sun	
	Should in the farthest east begin to draw	
	The shady curtains from Aurora's bed,	130
	Away from light steals home my heavy son,	
	And private in his chamber pens himself,	
	Shuts up his windows, locks fair daylight out,	
	And makes himself an artificial night.	
	Black and portentous must this humour prove,	135
	Unless good counsel may the cause remove.	
BENVOLIO	My noble uncle, do you know the cause?	
MONTAGUE	I neither know it, nor can learn of him.	
BENVOLIO	Have you importuned him by any means?	
MONTAGUE	Both by myself and many other friends:	140
	But he, his own affections' counsellor,	
	Is to himself – I will not say how true –	
	But to himself so secret and so close,	
	So far from sounding and discovery	
	As is the bud bit with an envious worm	145
	Ere he can spread his sweet leaves to the air,	
	Or dedicate his beauty to the sun.	
	Could we but learn from whence his sorrows grow,	
	We would as willingly give cure as know.	

Enter ROMEO.

BENVOLIO   See where he comes. So please you, step aside.   150
            I'll know his grievance or be much denied.

MONTAGUE   I would thou wert so happy by thy stay
            To hear true shrift. Come, madam, let's away.

Exit MONTAGUE, with LADY MONTAGUE.

BENVOLIO   Good morrow, cousin.

ROMEO   Is the day so young?

BENVOLIO   But new struck nine.

ROMEO   Ay me, sad hours seem long.   155
            Was that my father that went hence so fast?

BENVOLIO   It was. What sadness lengthens Romeo's hours?

ROMEO   Not having that which, having, makes them short.

BENVOLIO   In love?

ROMEO   Out –   160

BENVOLIO   Of love?

ROMEO   Out of her favour where I am in love.

BENVOLIO   Alas, that Love, so gentle in his view,
            Should be so tyrannous and rough in proof!

Act 2 Scene 2

JULIET   What man art thou, that thus bescreened in night
            So stumblest on my counsel?

ROMEO   By a name
            I know not how to tell thee who I am.
            My name, dear saint, is hateful to myself   55
            Because it is an enemy to thee.
            Had I it written, I would tear the word.

JULIET   My ears have yet not drunk a hundred words
            Of thy tongue's uttering, yet I know the sound.
            Art thou Romeo, and a Montague?   60

ROMEO   Neither, fair maid, if either thee dislike.

Turn over

JULIET	How cam'st thou hither, tell me, and wherefore?	
	The orchard walls are high and hard to climb –	
	And the place death, considering who thou art,	
	If any of my kinsmen find thee here.	65

ROMEO	With love's light wings did I o'erperch these walls,	
	For stony limits cannot hold love out –	
	And what love can do, that dares love attempt.	
	Therefore thy kinsmen are no stop to me.	

| JULIET | If they do see thee, they will murder thee. | 70 |

ROMEO	Alack, there lies more peril in thine eye	
	Than twenty of their swords. Look thou but sweet	
	And I am proof against their enmity.	

| JULIET | I would not for the world they saw thee here. | |

ROMEO	I have night's cloak to hide me from their eyes.	75
	And but thou love me, *let* them find me here.	
	My life were better ended by their hate	
	Than death proroguèd, wanting of thy love.	

| JULIET | By whose direction found'st thou out this place? | |

ROMEO	By love, that first did prompt me to inquire.	80
	He lent me counsel, and I lent him eyes.	
	I am no pilot, yet wert thou as far	
	As that vast shore washed with the farthest sea,	
	I should adventure for such merchandise.	

JULIET	Thou knowest the mask of night is on my face,	85
	Else would a maiden blush bepaint my cheek	
	For that which thou hast heard me speak tonight.	
	Fain would I dwell on form – fain, fain deny	
	What I have spoke. – But farewell compliment!	
	Dost thou love me? I know thou wilt say 'Ay' –	90
	And I will take thy word. Yet if thou swear'st	
	Thou mayst prove false. At lovers' perjuries	
	They say Jove laughs. O gentle Romeo,	
	If thou dost love, pronounce it faithfully.	
	Or if thou think I am too quickly won,	95
	I'll frown, and be perverse, and say thee nay,	
	So thou wilt woo – but else, not for the world.	
	In truth, fair Montague, I am too fond,	
	And therefore thou mayst think my 'haviour light.	
	But trust me, gentleman, I'll prove more true	100
	Than those that have more cunning to be strange.	
	I should have been more strange, I must confess,	
	But that thou overheard'st, ere I was ware,	
	My true-love passion. Therefore pardon me,	
	And not impute this yielding to light love,	105
	Which the dark night hath so discoverèd.	

| ROMEO | Lady, by yonder blessèd moon I vow, |
| | That tips with silver all these fruit-tree tops – |

JULIET	O swear not by the moon, th' inconstant moon,
	That monthly changes in her circled orb,	110
	Lest that thy love prove likewise variable.

| ROMEO | What shall I swear by? |

JULIET	Do not swear at all. –
	Or if thou wilt, swear by thy gracious self,
	Which is the god of my idolatry,
	And I'll believe thee.

| ROMEO | If my heart's dear love – | 115 |

JULIET	Well, do not swear. Although I joy in thee,
	I have no joy of this contract tonight.
	It is too rash, too unadvised, too sudden –
	Too like the lightning, which doth cease to be
	Ere one can say 'It lightens'. Sweet, good night.	120
	This bud of love, by summer's ripening breath,
	May prove a beauteous flower when next we meet.
	Good night, good night! As sweet repose and rest
	Come to thy heart as that within my breast.

| ROMEO | O wilt thou leave me so unsatisfied? | 125 |

| JULIET | What satisfaction canst thou have tonight? |

| ROMEO | Th' exchange of thy love's faithful vow for mine. |

| JULIET | I gave thee mine before thou didst request it – |
| | And yet I would it were to give again. |

| ROMEO | Would'st thou withdraw it? For what purpose, love? | 130 |

JULIET	But to be frank and give it thee again:
	And yet I wish but for the thing I have.
	My bounty is as boundless as the sea,
	My love as deep. The more I give to thee,
	The more I have, for both are infinite.	135

END OF TEST

Set

B

KEY STAGE 3
Levels 4–7

Shakespeare
Test Paper

English

Shakespeare Test Paper

Romeo and Juliet

Instructions:

- find a quiet place where you can sit down and complete the test paper undisturbed

- make sure you have all the necessary equipment to complete the test paper

- read the question carefully

- answer the question on lined paper

- go through and check your answer when you have finished writing

Time:

This test paper is **45 minutes** long.

You are being tested on your reading and understanding of the Shakespeare scenes you have studied.

Check how you have done against the mark scheme in the Instructions, Answers and Mark Scheme Booklet.

	Max. Mark	**Actual Mark**
Score	18	....

First name ....

Last name ....

Romeo and Juliet

You should spend about 45 minutes on this section.

Romeo and Juliet

In these scenes, Romeo thinks that, and behaves like, he is in love.

What do we learn about lovers' behaviour in these scenes?

Support your ideas by referring to both of the extracts which are printed on the following pages.

(18 marks)

Use the printed scenes to answer the question set on page 3.

Act 1 Scene 1

LADY MONTAGUE	O where is Romeo? Saw you him today?	110
	Right glad I am he was not at this fray.	
BENVOLIO	Madam, an hour before the worshipped sun	
	Peered forth the golden window of the east,	
	A troubled mind drove me to walk abroad –	
	Where, underneath the grove of sycamore	115
	That westward rooteth from this city side,	
	So early walking did I see your son.	
	Towards him I made, but he was ware of me,	
	And stole into the covert of the wood.	
	I, measuring his affections by my own,	120
	Which then most sought where most might not be found,	
	Being one too many by my weary self,	
	Pursued my humour not pursuing his,	
	And gladly shunned who gladly fled from me.	
MONTAGUE	Many a morning hath he there been seen,	125
	With tears augmenting the fresh morning's dew,	
	Adding to clouds more clouds with his deep sighs.	
	But all so soon as the all-cheering sun	
	Should in the farthest east begin to draw	
	The shady curtains from Aurora's bed,	130
	Away from light steals home my heavy son,	
	And private in his chamber pens himself,	
	Shuts up his windows, locks fair daylight out,	
	And makes himself an artificial night.	
	Black and portentous must this humour prove,	135
	Unless good counsel may the cause remove.	
BENVOLIO	My noble uncle, do you know the cause?	
MONTAGUE	I neither know it, nor can learn of him.	
BENVOLIO	Have you importuned him by any means?	
MONTAGUE	Both by myself and many other friends:	140
	But he, his own affections' counsellor,	
	Is to himself – I will not say how true –	
	But to himself so secret and so close,	
	So far from sounding and discovery	
	As is the bud bit with an envious worm	145
	Ere he can spread his sweet leaves to the air,	
	Or dedicate his beauty to the sun.	
	Could we but learn from whence his sorrows grow,	
	We would as willingly give cure as know.	

Enter ROMEO.

BENVOLIO	See where he comes. So please you, step aside.	150
	I'll know his grievance or be much denied.	

MONTAGUE   I would thou wert so happy by thy stay
             To hear true shrift. Come, madam, let's away.

Exit MONTAGUE, with LADY MONTAGUE.

BENVOLIO   Good morrow, cousin.

ROMEO   Is the day so young?

BENVOLIO   But new struck nine.

ROMEO   Ay me, sad hours seem long.   155
             Was that my father that went hence so fast?

BENVOLIO   It was. What sadness lengthens Romeo's hours?

ROMEO   Not having that which, having, makes them short.

BENVOLIO   In love?

ROMEO   Out –   160

BENVOLIO   Of love?

ROMEO   Out of her favour where I am in love.

BENVOLIO   Alas, that Love, so gentle in his view,
             Should be so tyrannous and rough in proof!

ROMEO   Alas, that Love, whose view is muffled still,   165
             Should without eyes see pathways to his will!
             Where shall we dine? O me! What fray was here?
             Yet tell me not, for I have heard it all.
             Here's much to do with hate, but more with love.
             Why then, O brawling love, O loving hate,   170
             O anything of nothing first create!
             O heavy lightness, serious vanity,
             Misshapen chaos of well-seeming forms!
             Feather of lead, bright smoke, cold fire, sick health,
             Still-waking sleep, that is not what it is!   175
             This love feel I, that feel no love in this.
             Dost thou not laugh?

BENVOLIO   No, coz, I rather weep.

Turn over

Act 2 Scene 2

JULIET   What man art thou, that thus bescreened in night
So stumblest on my counsel?

ROMEO   By a name
I know not how to tell thee who I am.
My name, dear saint, is hateful to myself   55
Because it is an enemy to thee.
Had I it written, I would tear the word.

JULIET   My ears have yet not drunk a hundred words
Of thy tongue's uttering, yet I know the sound.
Art thou Romeo, and a Montague?   60

ROMEO   Neither, fair maid, if either thee dislike.

JULIET   How cam'st thou hither, tell me, and wherefore?
The orchard walls are high and hard to climb –
And the place death, considering who thou art,
If any of my kinsmen find thee here.   65

ROMEO   With love's light wings did I o'erperch these walls,
For stony limits cannot hold love out –
And what love can do, that dares love attempt.
Therefore thy kinsmen are no stop to me.

JULIET   If they do see thee, they will murder thee.   70

ROMEO   Alack, there lies more peril in thine eye
Than twenty of their swords. Look thou but sweet
And I am proof against their enmity.

JULIET   I would not for the world they saw thee here.

ROMEO   I have night's cloak to hide me from their eyes.   75
And but thou love me, *let* them find me here.
My life were better ended by their hate
Than death proroguèd, wanting of thy love.

JULIET   By whose direction found'st thou out this place?

ROMEO   By love, that first did prompt me to inquire.   80
He lent me counsel, and I lent him eyes.
I am no pilot, yet wert thou as far
As that vast shore washed with the farthest sea,
I should adventure for such merchandise.

JULIET   Thou knowest the mask of night is on my face,   85
Else would a maiden blush bepaint my cheek
For that which thou hast heard me speak tonight.
Fain would I dwell on form – fain, fain deny
What I have spoke. – But farewell compliment!

	Dost thou love me? I know thou wilt say 'Ay' –	90
	And I will take thy word. Yet if thou swear'st	
	Thou mayst prove false. At lovers' perjuries	
	They say Jove laughs. O gentle Romeo,	
	If thou dost love, pronounce it faithfully.	
	Or if thou think I am too quickly won,	95
	I'll frown, and be perverse, and say thee nay,	
	So thou wilt woo – but else, not for the world.	
	In truth, fair Montague, I am too fond,	
	And therefore thou mayst think my 'haviour light.	
	But trust me, gentleman, I'll prove more true	100
	Than those that have more cunning to be strange	
	I should have been more strange, I must confess,	
	But that thou overheard'st, ere I was ware,	
	My true-love passion. Therefore pardon me,	
	And not impute this yielding to light love,	105
	Which the dark night hath so discoverèd.	

ROMEO   Lady, by yonder blessèd moon I vow,
               That tips with silver all these fruit-tree tops –

JULIET   O swear not by the moon, th' inconstant moon,
               That monthly changes in her circled orb,   110
               Lest that thy love prove likewise variable.

ROMEO   What shall I swear by?

JULIET   Do not swear at all. –
               Or if thou wilt, swear by thy gracious self,
               Which is the god of my idolatry,
               And I'll believe thee.

ROMEO   If my heart's dear love –   115

JULIET   Well, do not swear. Although I joy in thee,
               I have no joy of this contract tonight.
               It is too rash, too unadvised, too sudden –
               Too like the lightning, which doth cease to be
               Ere one can say 'It lightens'. Sweet, good night.   120
               This bud of love, by summer's ripening breath,
               May prove a beauteous flower when next we meet.
               Good night, good night! As sweet repose and rest
               Come to thy heart as that within my breast.

ROMEO   O wilt thou leave me so unsatisfied?   125

JULIET   What satisfaction canst thou have tonight?

ROMEO   Th' exchange of thy love's faithful vow for mine.

                              END OF TEST

Set
B

KEY STAGE 3
Levels 4–7

Writing Test
Paper

English

Monsters

Letts

Writing Test Paper

Monsters

Instructions:

- find a quiet place where you can sit down and complete the test paper undisturbed
- make sure you have all the necessary equipment to complete the test paper
- read the questions carefully
- answer the questions on lined paper
- go through and check your answers when you have finished writing

Time:

This test paper is **1 hour 15 minutes** long.

You should spend **30 minutes** on the short writing task, including planning time.

You should spend **45 minutes** on the long writing task, including planning time.

Write the answers on lined paper, then check how you have done against the mark scheme in the Instructions, Answers and Mark Scheme Booklet.

Short Writing Task

Strand	Max. Mark	Actual Mark
Sentence structure, punctuation and text organisation	6	
Composition and effect	10	
Spelling	4	

Long Writing Task

Strand	Max. Mark	Actual Mark
Sentence structure and punctuation	8	
Text structure and organisation	8	
Composition and effect	14	

First name ....

Last name ....

Writing Paper – Short Writing Task

Spend about 30 minutes on this section.

> You write ghost stories. You are about to start writing your next novel. The publisher wants you to write a convincing opening for your next story before they give you the money to go ahead and write it in full. The publisher wants you to write just the opening two or three paragraphs to show how you are going to get the reader's attention.

The publisher wants you to:

- Set the scene

- Create the mood

- End on a cliffhanger.

Write your opening, based on the ideas given above.

(20 marks, including 4 for spelling)

Writing Paper – Long Writing Task

Spend about 15 minutes planning your answer and 30 minutes writing.

Over the years, many people have reported sightings of ghosts and other supernatural events, but no one has been able to prove whether ghosts or other supernatural things actually exist or not.

Here are some reasons why people *don't* believe in ghosts and the supernatural.

- There is no scientific evidence to prove they exist.

- Often, they are witnessed by people alone, who could be making things up.

- Many of them have been proven to be fakes.

Here are some reasons why people *do* believe in ghosts and the supernatural.

- If only one of the thousands of cases is true, then they exist.

- There are many things that science cannot explain.

- People who have experienced them have been honest and trustworthy.

A Sunday magazine wants you to write an article arguing the case for and against ghosts existing, before you come to your own opinion. You can use the ideas above and any of your own ideas or examples, if you wish.

Write the article!

(30 marks)

END OF TEST

Set
B

KEY STAGE 3
Levels 4–7

Reading Test
Paper

English

Monsters

Reading Test Paper

Monsters

Instructions:

- find a quiet place where you can sit down and complete the test paper undisturbed

- make sure you have all the necessary equipment to complete the test paper

- read the questions carefully

- answer all the questions

- go through and check your answers when you have finished the test paper

Time:

This test paper is **1 hour 15 minutes** long.

You have **15 minutes** to read the Reading Booklet. During this time you are not allowed to open the Reading Paper to look at the questions.

You have **1 hour** to write the answers.

Write the answers in this booklet, then check how you have done against the mark scheme in the Instructions, Answers and Mark Scheme Booklet.

Page	3	5	7	Max. Mark	**Actual Mark**
Score	....	....	....	32	....

First name ....

Last name ....

1   From paragraphs one and two, give two features of Bigfoot.   *(2 marks)*   Q1

    i _____

    ii _____

2   a) In paragraph two, what does the word "apparently" suggest in this sentence –
       "*The first sighting of a Sasquatch by a white man apparently came in 1811*"?   *(1 mark)*   Q2a

       The word "apparently" suggests _____

       _____

    b) In paragraph two, why does the writer refer to "*strange footprints*"?   *(1 mark)*   Q2b

       _____

       _____

       _____

3   a) Here are the topics of the first four paragraphs. Match up the topic with the correct
       paragraph number.   *(2 marks)*   Q3a

Topic	Paragraph Number
A description of a captured Sasquatch	
An introduction to what Bigfoot is	
An explanation of what the captured Sasquatch might have been	
The first sightings of a Sasquatch	

    b) Explain why the text has quotations about personal experiences as well as dates and facts.
          (1 mark)   Q3b

       _____

       _____

       _____

4   How does the writer make you feel that Bigfoot is probably a fake? You should comment on the effect of:

• the historical examples chosen

• the writer's comments on those examples

• the language used by the writer.   *(5 marks)*

_____

_____

_____

_____

_____

_____

_____

_____

_____

_____

_____

_____

_____

_____

_____

_____

_____

_____

Turn over

5   a) From the first sentence, write down the phrase that shows the writer is confused.

(1 mark)

Q5a

_____

_____

_____

_____

    b) How does this phrase help to keep the reader's interest?   *(1 mark)*

Q5b

_____

_____

_____

_____

6   In the first paragraph, the writer describes "*these frowning walls and dark window openings*".
        What does the word "frowning" suggest about the walls?   *(1 mark)*

Q6

_____

_____

_____

_____

7   a) From paragraph three, identify one thing about the old man that suggests he is well-mannered.

(1 mark)

Q7a

_____

_____

    b) From paragraph four, identify one thing about the old man that suggests he is unusual
        or strange.   *(1 mark)*

Q7b

_____

_____

8   a) Paragraphs one and two and paragraphs three and four are about different characters and are
        written in different styles.

        Explain one difference in the way that they are written.   *(1 mark)*

        _____

        _____

        _____

        _____

        _____

        _____

    b) Explain how the fact that we don't know the old man's name at this point, or who he is, makes
        the story interesting.   *(1 mark)*

        _____

        _____

        _____

        _____

        _____

        _____

9   What do you learn about the writer's viewpoint and purpose from the passage? Show whether
        the following statements are TRUE or FALSE by writing T for TRUE or F for FALSE in each of
        the boxes.   *(2 marks)*

        The writer wants us to feel that the narrator is confident.   ☐

        The writer's aim is to entertain and interest the reader.   ☐

        The writer wants us to like the old man.   ☐

        The aim of the writer is to build up tension in the reader.   ☐

10   In the first two paragraphs, the writer gets the reader interested straight away by creating a
      feeling of mystery.

      Find two examples of where the writer does this and explain how each one makes the
      article mysterious.   *(2 marks)*

      i _____

      _____

      ii _____

      _____

Q10

11   In paragraph five (from *"The men ..."* to *"..in the Loch."*) the writer tries to make the reader
      feel that there might be some truth in the monster stories. Choose two different words or
      phrases and explain how they create this effect on the reader.   *(2 marks)*

Q11

Word/Phrase	Effect on the reader	How it creates this effect on the reader
	makes the reader think that there might be some truth in the monster stories	because it suggests
	makes the reader think that there might be some truth in the monster stories	because it suggests

12 a) In paragraph twelve, it says *"Several scientific studies have been conducted, including
       thorough sonar surveys of the Loch, and these have not revealed any presence of such a
       "monster".* Why does the writer use the word "thorough" in this sentence?   *(1 mark)*

       _____

       _____

Q12a

   b) Why is the word "monster" in inverted commas?   *(1 mark)*

       _____

       _____

Q12b

13   In this article, how does the writer use language and content to create a serious account about the monster?

You should comment on how the choice of content and language:

- makes the article sound scientific

- makes the article sound well researched

- includes a sense of mystery.   *(5 marks)*

Q13

_____

_____

_____

_____

_____

_____

_____

_____

_____

_____

_____

_____

_____

_____

_____

_____

_____

_____

END OF TEST

subtotal

Set **B**

KEY STAGE 3
Levels 4–7

Reading Booklet

English

Monsters

Monsters

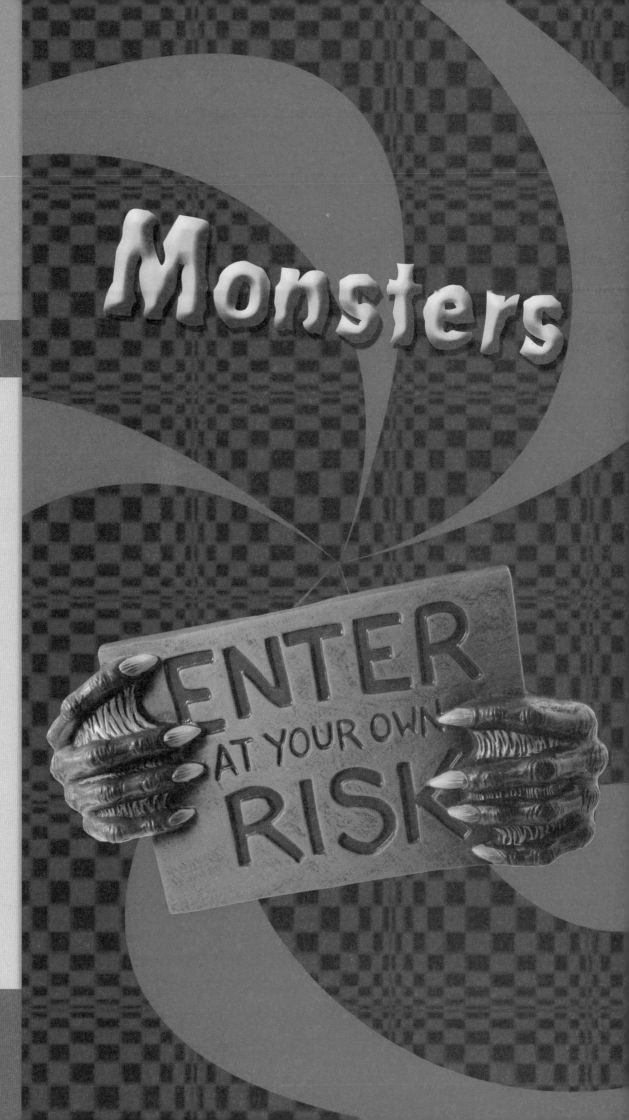

ENTER
AT YOUR OWN
RISK

Letts

Contents

Bigfoot
of North America

1   If the Himalayas of Asia has its Yeti, the Pacific Northwest of
    America has its Bigfoot: a hairy, ape-like, biped that stands
    seven to nine feet tall and weighs between 600
    and 900 pounds.

2   Bigfoot, or as it's often called in Canada, the *Sasquatch*, is mentioned in several
    native American legends. In fact, the term "Sasquatch" is Indian for "hairy
    giant". The first sighting of a Sasquatch footprint by a white man apparently
    came in 1811 near what is now the town of Jasper, Alberta, Canada. A trader
    named David Thompson found some strange footprints, fourteen inches long
    and eight inches wide, with four toes, in the snow.

3   In 1884 the newspaper, *Daily Colonist*, of Victoria, British Columbia,
    told of the capture of a "Sasquatch". The creature was spotted by
    a train crew along the Fraser River. The crew stopped the train,
    gave chase, and captured the animal after following it up a rocky
    hill. The creature was given the name "Jacko" and was
    "… something of the gorilla type, standing four feet seven
    inches in height and weighing 127 pounds. He has long, black,
    strong hair and resembles a human being, with one exception –

his entire body, excepting his hands (or paws) and feet, are covered with glossy hair about one inch long … he possesses extraordinary strength, as he will take hold of a stick and break it by wrenching it or twisting it, which no man could break in the same way."

4   The description of Jacko is so much like that of a chimpanzee, and so unlike later Bigfoot reports, that some have suggested the animal actually was a chimpanzee. If brought back by a sailor from Africa, the animal might have escaped or been turned loose. There is also the strong possibility that the entire story was a hoax. Newspapers of that era often printed hoax stories to amuse their readers (perhaps not unlike some tabloids sold today).

5   Rumours about the Sasquatch continued through the end of the century. Then, in 1910, the murder of two miners, found with their heads cut off, was attributed to the creatures, though there was little supporting evidence that the killing wasn't human in origin. In any case, the place of the murders, Nahanni Valley, in Canada, was changed to Headless Valley, because of the incident.

6   Interest in Bigfoot began to pick up in the United States in 1958 when a bulldozer operator named Jerry Crew found enormous footprints around where he was working in Humboldt County, California. Crew made a cast of the footprint. A local newspaper ran the story of Crew and his footprint with a photo. The story was picked up by other papers and ran throughout the country. It was the picture of Crew holding the "Bigfoot" that made the name stick.

7   In 1967 Roger Patterson and Bob Gimlin, Bigfoot buffs, announced they'd captured Bigfoot with a movie camera. They filmed a few seconds of an ape-like creature, apparently female, moving across a clearing near Bluff Creek in northern California. While the film is not perfectly clear, there is no mistaking the creature in the film for a common animal. The movie shows either a real Bigfoot, or a man in a clever costume. Nobody has ever proved the film fake, though some viewers were suspicious about the unnatural stride the creature had. One scientist who viewed the film, John Napier, of the Smithsonian Institution, admitted, "I couldn't see the zipper, and I still can't."

8   Scientists have a right to be suspicious of Bigfoot evidence. Two known hoax films exist. A controversial carcass, the "Minnesota Iceman", was thought to be a hoax, too. In addition, hoax footprints have been made from fake wooden feet and altered boots. One company even produced a set of oversized plastic strap-on feet that you could use to fool your friends and family.

With kind permission of Lee Krystek © Lee Krystek
unmuseum.org/bigfoot.htm

Dracula

1   **I** **stood in silence where I was, for I did not know what to do. Of bell or knocker there was no sign.** Through these frowning walls and dark window openings it was not likely that my voice could penetrate. The time I waited seemed endless, and I felt doubts and fears crowding upon me. What sort of place had I come to, and among what kind of people? What sort of grim adventure was it on which I had embarked? Was this a customary incident in the life of a solicitor's clerk sent out to explain the purchase of a London estate to a foreigner? Solicitor's clerk! Mina would not like that. Solicitor, for just before leaving London I got word that my examination was successful, and I am now a full-blown solicitor! I began to rub my eyes and pinch myself to see if I were awake. It all seemed like a horrible nightmare to me, and I expected that I should suddenly awake, and find myself at home, with the dawn struggling in through the windows, as I had now and again felt in the morning after a day of overwork. But my flesh answered the pinching test, and my eyes were not to be deceived. I was indeed awake and among the Carpathians. All I could do now was to be patient, and to wait the coming of morning.

2   Just as I had come to this conclusion I heard a heavy step approaching behind the great door, and saw through the chinks the gleam of a coming light. Then there was the sound of rattling chains and the clanking of massive bolts drawn back. A key was turned with the loud grating noise of long disuse, and the great door swung back.

3   Within, stood a tall old man, clean shaven save for a long white moustache, and clad in black from head to foot, without a single speck of colour about him anywhere. He held in his hand an antique silver lamp, in which the flame burned without a chimney or globe of any kind, throwing long quivering shadows as it flickered in the draught of the open door. The old man motioned me in with his right hand with a courtly gesture, saying in excellent English, but with a strange intonation.

4   "Welcome to my house! Enter freely and of your own free will!" He made no motion of stepping to meet me, but stood like a statue, as though his gesture of welcome had fixed him into stone. The instant, however, that I had stepped over the threshold, he moved impulsively forward, and holding out his hand grasped mine with a strength which made me wince, an effect which was not lessened by the fact that it seemed cold as ice, more like the hand of a dead than a living man.

From Chapter 2 of *Dracula* by Bram Stoker

The Loch Ness Monster

1   The Loch Ness Monster is supposedly living in Scotland's Loch (Lake) Ness. "Nessie", as she is called, is the best known cryptozoological creature in the world.

2   Carvings of this unidentified animal, made by the ancient inhabitants of the Scottish Highlands some 1,500 years ago, are the earliest evidence that Loch Ness harbours a strange aquatic creature.

3   The earliest recorded sighting of the Loch Ness Monster was in the biography of St. Columba by Adamnan in the year 565 AD. The monster apparently attacked and killed a man who was swimming in the River Ness.

4   The monster didn't make headlines again until August 27, 1930 when 3 fishermen reported seeing a disturbance in the water. The men watched as a creature 20 feet long approached their boat throwing water in the air. As it passed them, its wake caused their boat to rock violently.

5   The men were convinced that the disturbance was caused by a living creature. Following the story, the newspaper received several letters from people claiming also to have seen a strange creature in the Loch.

6   In 1962, The Loch Ness Investigation Bureau was formed to act as a research organization and clearing house for information about the creature. In the beginning they only conducted research for a few weeks in the year, but by 1964 they established a more permanent presence around the Loch. Eventually the Bureau established camera stations with both still and cinema cameras with telephoto lenses. They had vans which served as mobile camera stations, and underwater listening devises. Searches were conducted using hot-air balloons and infrared night-time cameras, sonar scanners and submarines.

7   A great deal of information was discovered about the Loch, but they have yet to produce any concrete evidence of a monster.

8   Loch Ness is located in the north of Scotland and is one of a series of interlinked lochs which run along the Great Glen. The Great Glen is a distinctive incision which runs across the country and represents a large geological fault zone. The interlinking was completed in the 19th century following the completion of the Caledonian Canal.

9   The Great Glen is more than 700 ft (213 m) deep and ice free. It is fed by the Oich and other streams and drained by the Ness to the Moray Firth. It forms part of the Caledonian Canal. By volume, Loch Ness is the largest freshwater lake in Great Britain.

10   Since December 1933, when newspapers published accounts of a "monster", 40 to 50 ft (12–15 m) long, said to have been seen in the Loch, there have been alleged sightings.

11   As a result of the publicity, Loch Ness has become a major tourist attraction.

12   Several scientific studies have been conducted, including thorough sonar surveys of the Loch, and these have not revealed any presence of such a "monster".

13   Many people believe that the size and great depth of the Loch, together with potential underwater caves, gives the monster many places to hide.

14   Most of the Nessie witnesses describe something with two humps, a tail, and a snake-like head. A V-shape was often mentioned, as well as a gaping red mouth and horns or antennae on the top of the creature's head. Nessie's movements have been studied, and the films and photos analysed to determine what Nessie might be, if she exists.

15   There are numerous theories as to Nessie's identity, including a snake-like primitive whale known as a zeuglodon, a type of long-necked aquatic seal, giant eels, walruses, floating mats of plants, giant molluscs, otters, a "paraphysical" entity, mirages, and diving birds, but many lake monster researchers seem to favour the plesiosaur theory. The case has occasionally been supported by indistinct photographic evidence – though – in 1994 – a famous 1934 photograph was revealed to be a hoax.

From http://crystalinks.com/loch_ness/html

Set
C

KEY STAGE 3
Levels 4–7

Writing Test
Paper

English

Down South

Writing Test Paper

Down South

Instructions:

- find a quiet place where you can sit down and complete the test paper undisturbed
- make sure you have all the necessary equipment to complete the test paper
- read the questions carefully
- answer the questions on lined paper
- go through and check your answers when you have finished writing

Time:

This test paper is **1 hour 15 minutes** long.

You should spend **30 minutes** on the short writing task, including planning time.

You should spend **45 minutes** on the long writing task, including planning time.

Write the answers on lined paper, then check how you have done against the mark scheme in the Instructions, Answers and Mark Scheme Booklet.

Short Writing Task

Strand	Max. Mark	Actual Mark
Sentence structure, punctuation and text organisation	6	
Composition and effect	10	
Spelling	4	

Long Writing Task

Strand	Max. Mark	Actual Mark
Sentence structure and punctuation	8	
Text structure and organisation	8	
Composition and effect	14	

First name

Last name

Writing Paper – Short Writing Task

Spend about 30 minutes on this section.

You have just returned from a holiday which turned out to be a nightmare. The following things went wrong.

> Your flights were delayed by 30 hours and you had to sleep in the airport lounge.
>
> When you arrived, your rooms had been double-booked and were taken.
>
> All your family got food-poisoning from the hotel's own food.

Write a letter to your local newspaper about what happened.

Analyse what went wrong and comment on the company you used.

You do not need to put any addresses – just start your letter with "Dear Sir or Madam".

Write the letter.

(20 marks, including 4 for spelling)

Writing Paper – Long Writing Task

Spend about 15 minutes planning your answer and 30 minutes writing.

Your local council have allocated a large part of their budget to attracting more tourists to your area. You are the council's publicity officer and it is your job to write the text for the brochure. You need to persuade tourists to visit your area.

In your brochure, you need to do these things.

- Tell people what your area has to offer them.

- Describe your area honestly, but make it sound as good as possible without telling lies!

- Sell your area to those people it might appeal to. Old or young? Single or married?

The council **DO NOT** need you to **design** the brochure – they **just** want you to write the text for it.

Write the text for your brochure.

(30 marks)

END OF TEST

Set C

KEY STAGE 3
Levels 4–7

Reading Test
Paper

English

Down South

Reading Test Paper

Down South

Instructions:

- find a quiet place where you can sit down and complete the test paper undisturbed

- make sure you have all the necessary equipment to complete the test paper

- read the questions carefully

- answer all the questions

- go through and check your answers when you have finished the test paper

Time:

This test paper is **1 hour 15 minutes** long.

You have **15 minutes** to read the Reading Booklet. During this time you are not allowed to open the Reading Paper to look at the questions.

You have **1 hour** to write the answers.

Write the answers in this booklet, then check how you have done against the mark scheme in the Instructions, Answers and Mark Scheme Booklet.

Page	3	5	7	Max. Mark	**Actual Mark**
Score	....	....	....	32	....

First name ....

Last name ....

1   From paragraph one, give two different things that Jean Lafitte was well known for. *(2 marks)*

☐ Q1

i _____

ii _____

2   In paragraphs two and four, what does the choice of words in the following phrases suggest about Jean Lafitte?

a) *"Lafitte was a colourful character"*   *(1 mark)*

☐ Q2a

suggests _____

_____

b) *"he is accounted as a great romantic figure in Cajun Louisiana"*   *(1 mark)*

☐ Q2b

suggests _____

_____

3   a) The article is split into a number of paragraphs. Each paragraph has a topic. Fill in the table with the missing paragraph numbers.   *(2 marks)*

☐ Q3a

Topic	Paragraph Number
The end of Jean Lafitte's life	
Two places that exist today, connected to Jean Lafitte	
A summary of Jean Lafitte's main achievements	
The history of a diary about Jean Lafitte	
A place named after Jean Lafitte	
Reasons why Jean Lafitte became famous	

b) Give one reason why the text contains so many facts and very few opinions.   *(1 mark)*

☐ Q3b

_____

_____

4   How does the writer try to give the reader a fair view of the story of Jean Lafitte? You should comment on the effect of:

- The language used to describe Jean Lafitte and his life

- The use of facts and dates

- The content of the writing   *(5 marks)*

Q4

_____

_____

_____

_____

_____

_____

_____

_____

_____

_____

_____

_____

_____

_____

_____

Turn over

subtotal

5   a) From the sentence at the start of paragraph one, write down one word which suggests that
       the boat is moving slowly but effortlessly.   *(1 mark)*

☐ Q5a

_____

    b) What does the word *"gruesome"* suggest in paragraph one?   *(1 mark)*

☐ Q5b

_____

_____

_____

_____

6   In paragraph one, the writer says *"The immigrants crowded the rail as the quivering ship
       moved into the Mississippi River ..."* What does the phrase *"crowded the rail"* suggest about
       the people?   *(1 mark)*

☐ Q6

_____

_____

_____

_____

_____

7   From the whole text, identify two bad things about New Orleans.   *(2 marks)*

☐ Q7

    i _____

       _____

       _____

    ii _____

       _____

       _____

8   a) This story is divided by a sub-heading: "*A demon in the backhouse*". Which event has the
        writer chosen to leave out and not describe, where the sub-heading is?   *(1 mark)*

_____

_____

    b) Explain how the first paragraph prepares us for the fact that the accordion maker's arrival in
        New Orleans was not going to be easy?   *(1 mark)*

_____

_____

_____

_____

_____

_____

_____

9   What do you learn about the writer's viewpoint and purpose from the passage? Show whether
        the following statements are TRUE or FALSE by writing T for TRUE or F for FALSE in each of
        the boxes.   *(2 marks)*

The writer wants us to be aware that New Orleans is a smelly place.

The writer wants the reader to feel like the accordion maker.

The aim of the writer is to scare the reader.

The aim of the writer is to put people off visiting New Orleans.

Turn over

10   The web-page begins *"New Orleans seduces with Caribbean colour and waves of sultry southern heat."*

Explain two ways that this sentence makes the reader want to read more. Support each answer with a quotation from the sentence.   *(2 marks)*   Q10

i   _____

_____

ii _____

_____

11   Paragraph one, from *"Enshrouding us ..."* to the end of paragraph two, *"New Orleans is it,"* makes us feel that New Orleans is an exciting place but with a darker side. Choose two different words or phrases and explain how they create this effect on the reader.   *(2 marks)*   Q11

Word/Phrase	Effect on the reader	How it creates this effect on the reader
	makes the reader think that New Orleans is exciting	because it suggests
	makes the reader think that New Orleans has a darker side	because it suggests

12   In the fourth paragraph, it says *"New Orleans comprises a checkerboard of neighbourhoods of different wealth and ethnicity"*.

a) Why is New Orleans compared to a checkerboard?   *(1 mark)*   Q12a

_____

_____

b) In paragraph five, the word "suburbs" is in brackets. Why?   *(1 mark)*   Q12b

_____

_____

13 How is language used in the whole text to make New Orleans sound like an exciting place to visit?

You should comment on how the choice of words and phrases:

- makes New Orleans sound lively

- makes New Orleans sound mysterious

- makes New Orleans sound historical and cultured.

(5 marks)

_____

_____

_____

_____

_____

_____

_____

_____

_____

_____

_____

_____

_____

_____

_____

_____

_____

_____

END OF TEST

Set C

KEY STAGE 3
Levels 4–7

Reading Booklet

English

Down South

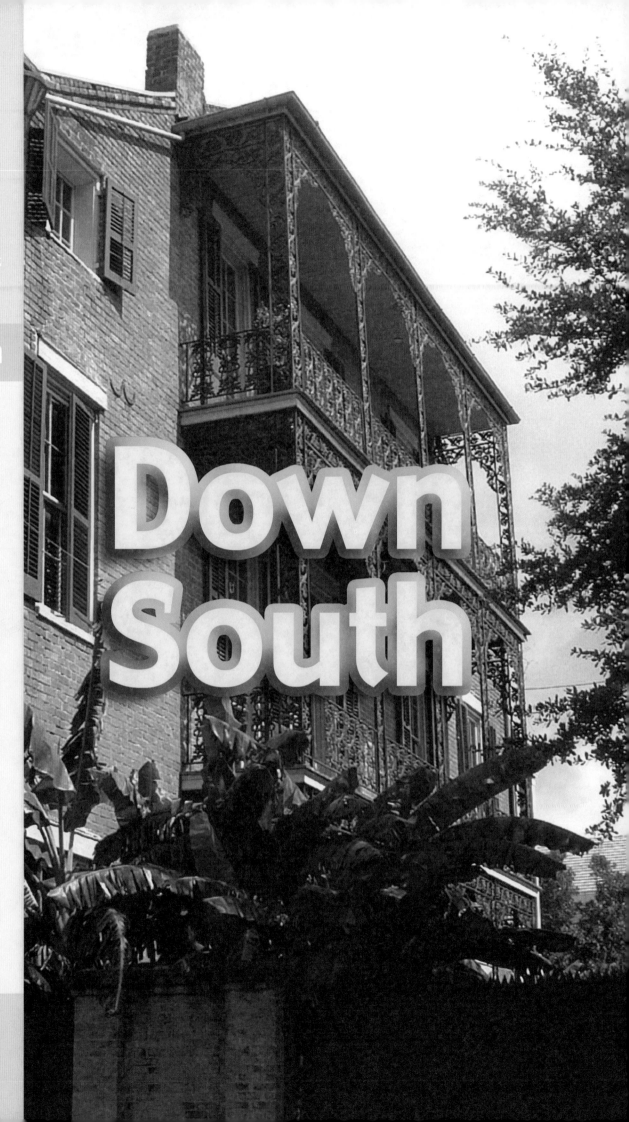

Down South

Letts

Contents

Jean Lafitte

1 Jean Lafitte or Laffite (*ca*1780 – *ca*1826?), was a pirate in the Gulf of Mexico in the early 19th century. He established his own "kingdom" of Barataria in the swamps and bayous near New Orleans after the Louisiana Purchase of 1803. He claimed to command more than 1000 men and provided them as troops for the Battle of New Orleans (1815). Afterwards he engaged in the slave trade after it had been banned.

2 Lafitte was a colourful character, said to have been born in France. He engaged in smuggling and privateering, with his "Kingdom of Barataria" (in what is now Louisiana) recognising the sovereignty of no other nation.

3 A controversial manuscript, known as the "Journal" of Jean Laffite, relates how, after his announced death in the 1820s, he lived in several states in the United States, raised a family and wrote this journal. At his request the publication of the journal was delayed for 100 years. In the 1950s the journal was translated from the French language and published. The original manuscript was purchased by Texas Governor Price Daniel and is on display at the Sam Houston Regional Library and Archives in Liberty, Texas.

4 Lafitte claimed never to have plundered an American vessel, and though he engaged in the contraband slave trade, he is accounted as a great romantic figure in Cajun Louisiana. His legend was perpetuated in Cecil B. DeMille's classic, *The Buccaneer* and even by a poem of Byron:

> *He left a corsair's name to other times,*
> *Linked one virtue to a thousand crimes.*

5 After the War of 1812, Lafitte or Laffite was active in the Neutral strip of coast between Spanish Texas and American Louisiana, left unoccupied and lawless until 1821.

6 His later years are obscure; a man many said was Lafitte died in Yucatan.

7 A U.S. National Park is named after him, in six physically separate sites in southeastern Louisiana, interpreting the local Acadian culture. The Barataria Preserve (in Jefferson Parish, Louisiana) interprets the natural and cultural history of the uplands, swamps, and marshlands of the region. Six miles southeast of New Orleans is the Chalmette Battlefield and National Cemetery, actual site of the 1815 battle and the final resting place for soldiers from the Civil War, Spanish – American War, World Wars I and II, and Vietnam.

8 **Jean Lafitte** is the name of a Cajun fishing village and tourist spot sited on Bayou Barataria.

With thanks to www.fact-index.com/j/je/jean_lafitte.html

Arriving in

¹ They coasted into the delta, breathed its odour of mud and wood smoke under sunset clouds, gold curls combed out of the west, or the powdered stamens of a broad-throated flower. In the dusk they could see flickering lights in the side channels, sometimes hear a gruesome roar – the alligators, said a deckhand; no, a cow bogged in mud, said the woman with the nephews. The immigrants crowded the rail as the quivering ship moved into the Mississippi River, within the pincer of land. Silvano stood next to his father. A red moon crawled out of the east. On the shore the boy heard a horse snort. Hours before New Orleans the odour of the city reached them – a fetid stink of cesspools and the smell of burning sugar.

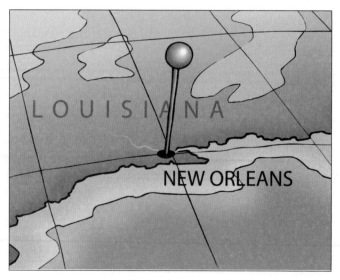

A demon in the backhouse

² Nothing went as the accordion maker anticipated. The young man from the train was not at the dock. They waited hours for him while the other passengers disappeared into the teeming streets.

³ "True friends are as rare as white flies," said the accordion maker bitterly. Silvano gaped at the black men and especially the women, whose heads were wrapped in turbans as though they concealed emeralds and rubies and chains of gold beneath the winded cloth. They puzzled their way along the noisy, thronged streets with the young man's map and found Decatur Street, but there was no number 16 there, only charred timbers among rampant fireweed, a gap in the row of frowsty tenements. The accordion maker forced his courage, spoke to an approaching man who looked Sicilian; at least his hair appeared Sicilian.

⁴ "Excuse me, I seek a boardinghouse, number sixteen, but it seems there is no building here – " The man did not answer, spat to his right as he passed. Silvano saw the punishment for not knowing American. The man must be American – one who despised Sicilians ...

New Orleans

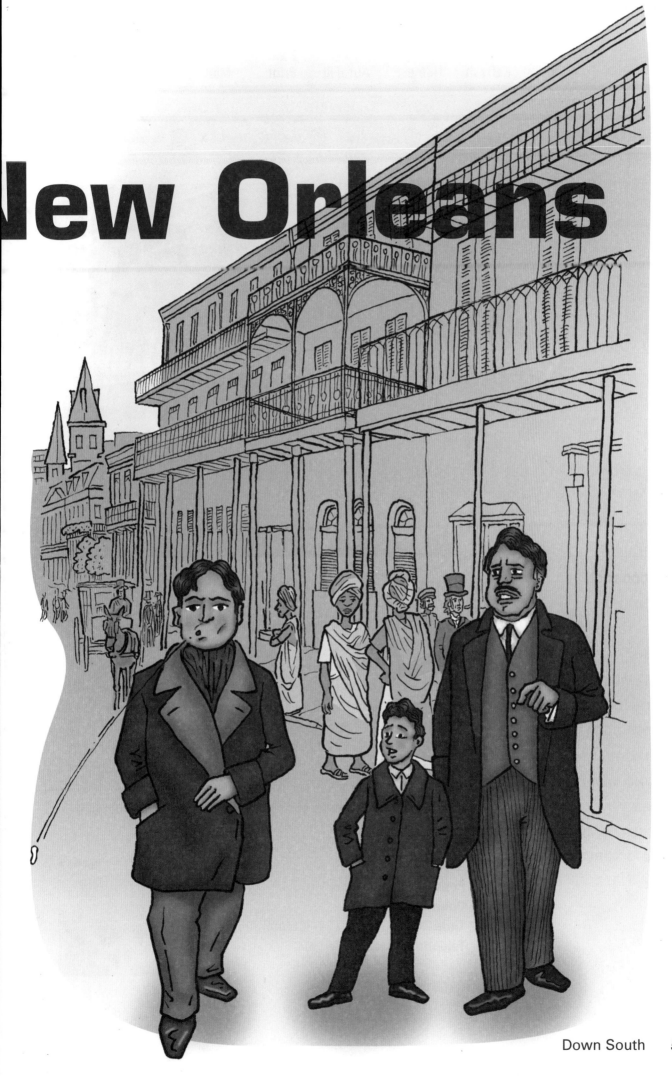

From Accordion Crimes, by E. Annie Proulx
Reprinted by permission of HarperCollins Publishers Ltd ©E. Annie Proulx 1997

Back Forward Stop Refresh Home AutoFill Print Mail

Address: @ www.lonelyplanet.com › go

@ Live Home Page @ Apple @ Apple Support @ Apple Store @ .Mac @ Mac OS X @ Microsoft MacTopia »

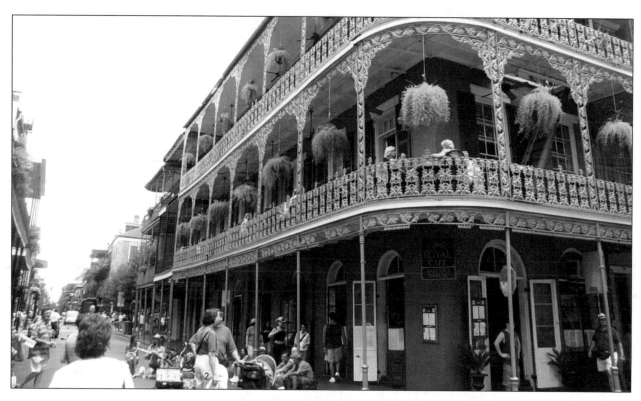

Favorites · History · Search · Scrapbook · Page Holder

New Orleans

1 New Orleans seduces with Caribbean colour and waves of sultry southern heat. Enshrouding us in dreams and ancient melodies, its sweet-tasting cocktails are laced with voodoo potions. The unofficial state motto, *laissez les bons temps rouler* ("let the good times roll"), pretty much says it all.

2 Called by some "The City That Care Forgot," New Orleans has a well-earned reputation for excess and debauchery. It's a cultural gumbo of African, Indian, Cajun and Creole influences. Whether you're looking for history, drama and intrigue or just a damn good bop in the street, New Orleans is it.

Area: 468 sq km
Population: 1.2 million
Country: USA
Time Zone: GMT/UTC -6 (Central Time)
Telephone Area Code: 504

BACK TO TOP

3 At the big toe of boot-shaped Louisiana, New Orleans nestles between Lake Pontchartrain, a huge but shallow body of saltwater that forms the northern edge of town, and a meniscus-shaped bend of the Mississippi River, about 145 river kilometres (90 miles) above where it empties into the Gulf of Mexico. The original and most visited portions of the city parallel the northern riverbank. Directions upriver or downriver are relative to the water flow, which bends maddeningly to all points of the compass. The Mississippi and Lake Pontchartrain also provide "riverside" or "lakeside" orientation.

4 New Orleans comprises a checkerboard of neighborhoods of different wealth and ethnicity – it's often only a few steps from ghetto to endowed estates. At the easternmost point of the city's crescent-shaped core is the heart of the original city, the French Quarter. To the southwest, the Uptown area encompasses the Garden District, universities and palatial mansions along the St Charles Ave Streetcar Line, which leads to the Riverbend area at the other end of the crescent.

5 Older *faubourgs* (suburbs) border the crowded French Quarter – to the east, the Faubourg Marigny appeals to a bohemian, mostly gay crowd, while the more down-at-heels Faubourg Tremé to the north is a black neighborhood known for its music. Downriver from Faubourg Marigny is the Bywater, a burgeoning artist hangout in an otherwise marginal district.

6 New Orleans International Airport (MSY) is 18 km (11 miles) west of the city center in Kenner, while both trains and buses share New Orleans Union Passenger Terminal ("Union Station") on Loyola Ave in the Central Business District (CBD), between the French Quarter and the Uptown area.

7 West of New Orleans you'll find the Cajun wetlands, an area of French patois-speaking rural people who still depend on the natural resources of the swamps. The Cajuns' Spanish counterparts, the Isleños, live in the coastal fishing villages south of New Orleans. Upstream along the Mississippi River, antebellum sugar plantations attract visitors who marvel at elegant plantation homes. An occasional slave cabin remains as a reminder of how the wealth was gained.

BACK TO TOP

Used with kind permission of www.lonelyplanet.com

Set

A

KEY STAGE 3
Levels 4–7

Writing Test
Paper

English

Food!

Writing Test Paper

Food!

Instructions:

- find a quiet place where you can sit down and complete the test paper undisturbed
- make sure you have all the necessary equipment to complete the test paper
- read the questions carefully
- answer the questions on lined paper
- go through and check your answers when you have finished writing

Time:

This test paper is **1 hour 15 minutes** long.

You should spend **30 minutes** on the short writing task, including planning time.

You should spend **45 minutes** on the long writing task, including planning time.

Write the answers on lined paper, then check how you have done against the mark scheme in the Instructions, Answers and Mark Scheme Booklet.

Short Writing Task

Strand	Max. Mark	Actual Mark
Sentence structure, punctuation and text organisation	6	
Composition and effect	10	
Spelling	4	

Long Writing Task

Strand	Max. Mark	Actual Mark
Sentence structure and punctuation	8	
Text structure and organisation	8	
Composition and effect	14	

First name

Last name

Writing Paper – Short Writing Task

Spend about 30 minutes on this section.

You write reviews for a school magazine – this week you have been asked to write a review of one of last week's school dinners.

Here is last week's menu.

Day	Main Course	Dessert
Monday	Fish and Chips	Ice-Cream
Tuesday	Cabbage Pie & Mashed Potatoes	Grapefruit Surprise
Wednesday	Broccoli & Cucumber Salad	Rhubarb Crumble
Thursday	Pizza	Melon Juice
Friday	Chicken Curry	Chocolate Sticky Pudding

In your review, the school magazine editor wants you to:

• analyse what was in the meal

• comment on what you thought about it.

Write your review on one of the school dinners above.

(20 marks, including 4 for spelling)

Writing Paper – Long Writing Task

Spend about 15 minutes planning your answer and 30 minutes writing.

Your local area has been named the least healthy in the whole country. You are a local newspaper journalist and you have been given the job of writing an article telling people about this and persuading them to adopt a more healthy lifestyle. Here are some of the facts that you have been given.

> 75% of the people in your area do not take regular exercise.
>
> 85% of the people in your area eat junk food, on average, four times a week.
>
> 60% of the people in your area visit the doctor once a month.
>
> The average life expectancy for men and women is five years below the national average.

Your editor wants you to write an article to:

• advise people about the situation in your area

• persuade them to change their ways.

Write the article!

(30 marks)

END OF TEST

Set
A

KEY STAGE 3
Levels 4–7

Reading Test
Paper

English

Food!

Reading Test Paper

Food!

Instructions:

- find a quiet place where you can sit down and complete the test paper undisturbed

- make sure you have all the necessary equipment to complete the test paper

- read the questions carefully

- answer all the questions

- go through and check your answers when you have finished the test paper

Time:

This test paper is **1 hour 15 minutes** long.

You have **15 minutes** to read the Reading Booklet. During this time you are not allowed to open the Reading Paper to look at the questions.

You have **1 hour** to write the answers.

Write the answers in this booklet, then check how you have done against the mark scheme in the Instructions, Answers and Mark Scheme Booklet.

Page	3	5	7	Max. Mark	Actual Mark
Score	....	....	....	32	....

First name   ....

Last name   ....

1   From the first three paragraphs, give two examples of what the Italian government wants to do.

(2 marks)   Q1

i _____

ii _____

2   a) In paragraph one, what does the choice of words in the following phrase suggest about the
       Italian government?
       "Italy is planning to crack down on chefs making bad copies of pizzas"   *(1 mark)*   Q2a

       "crack down" suggests _____

       _____

     b) What do the words *"fed up"*, *"'cos"* and *"they're"* suggest about the writer's audience?

       (1 mark)   Q2b

       _____

       _____

3   a) The article is split into paragraphs with different topics. Complete this table by writing the
       correct paragraph number in the box next to the paragraph's topic.   *(2 marks)*   Q3a

Topic	Paragraph Number
Rules about the pizza	
How the Margherita pizza got its name	
A reaction from a top pizza chef	
An introduction to the article	

     b) Explain one reason why the text has paragraphs with personal comments as well as
       paragraphs about historical background.   *(1 mark)*   Q3b

       _____

       _____

       _____

4   How does the article try to appeal to young people?
     You should comment on the effect of:

     • the language used

     • the length of paragraphs

     • the content of the article.   *(5 marks)*

_____

_____

_____

_____

_____

_____

_____

_____

_____

_____

_____

_____

_____

_____

_____

_____

_____

_____

Turn over

5 a) From the first part of the first sentence, *"Oliver Twist and his companions suffered the tortures of slow starvation for three months"*, write down one word which suggests that the boys are suffering.   *(1 mark)*

☐ Q5a

_____

   b) What is the effect of this word?   *(1 mark)*

☐ Q5b

_____

_____

_____

_____

6   In the second sentence, it says *"He had a wild, hungry eye"*. What does the phrase "hungry eye" suggest about the boy's character?   *(1 mark)*

☐ Q6

_____

_____

_____

_____

7 a) From the whole text, identify one feature of Oliver Twist's character.   *(1 mark)*

☐ Q7a

_____

_____

_____

   b) From the whole text, identify one feature of the master's character.   *(1 mark)*

☐ Q7b

_____

_____

_____

8   a) The extract from the story begins with long paragraphs and ends with short paragraphs.
        Explain one reason why this is.   *(1 mark)*

_____

_____

_____

_____

_____

    b) Explain how the line ' *"Please, sir," replied Oliver, "I want some more"* ' makes you feel sorry
        for Oliver.   *(1 mark)*

_____

_____

_____

_____

_____

_____

9   What do you learn about the writer's viewpoint and purpose from the passage? Show whether
        the following statements are TRUE or FALSE by writing T for TRUE or F for FALSE in each of
        the boxes.   *(2 marks)*

        The writer wants us to feel sorry for Oliver.   ☐

        The writer is trying to criticise the way that boys like Oliver
        were treated by authority.   ☐

        The writer is trying to give a factual historical account.   ☐

        The writer is trying to entertain the reader.   ☐

Turn over

10   Explain two ways that the first paragraph gives us information. Support each explanation
with a quotation.   *(2 marks)*   ☐ Q10

i   _____

_____

_____

ii _____

_____

_____

11   How does the writer, in paragraphs three and four, try to convince the reader that drinking
water is important? Choose two different words or phrases and explain how they create this
effect on the reader.   *(2 marks)*   ☐ Q11

Word/Phrase	Effect on the reader	How it creates this effect on the reader
	makes the reader think that drinking water is important	because it suggests
	makes the reader think that drinking water is important	because it suggests

12 a) In paragraph five, what is described as the main effect of caffeine?   *(1 mark)*   ☐ Q12a

_____

_____

_____

b) Why are brackets used at the start of paragraph five in the phrase *"Drinks that contain caffeine
(such as tea, coffee and cola)"*?   *(1 mark)*   ☐ Q12b

_____

_____

_____

13 In this web-page, how are language, grammar and content used to influence the reader?
    You should comment in your answer on the effect of the following.

    • The use of scientific words and phrases.

    • Sentence lengths.

    • The use of facts.   *(5 marks)*

Q13

_____

_____

_____

_____

_____

_____

_____

_____

_____

_____

_____

_____

_____

_____

_____

_____

_____

_____

_____

_____

                              END OF TEST

subtotal

Set **A**

KEY STAGE 3
Levels 4–7

Reading Booklet

English

Food!

Letts

Food!

Contents

Italy attempts to ban fake pizzas

1 Italy is planning to crack down on chefs making bad copies of pizza 'cos they're fed up with poor imitations.

2 The government wants strict rules on how a pizza should be made if it's to be called a Neapolitan pizza.

3 The new law will include a step-by-step guide to the perfect pizza, covering shape, depth, toppings and the way olive oil must be poured on top.

4 Pizza police will visit restaurants to make sure they stick to the rules, to guarantee their pizzas are genuine.

5 The rules about the pizza include:
   • must be round and no more than 35cm in diameter
   • must be cooked in a wood-fired oven
   • must be kneaded and shaped by hand
   • dough should be allowed to rise for at least six hours.

6 Top pizza chefs in Italy are delighted their famous food is going to be recognised and protected.

7 "Pizza is not just a food, it's a way of life," said pizza chef Vittorio Triunfo.

Made in Naples

8 Pizza is thought to have been invented in southern Italy in a place called Naples.

9 The famous Margherita was named after a queen of the same name and is topped with tomato, mozzarella and basil, the same colours as the Italian flag.

10 There are 23,000 pizzerias – special pizza restaurants – cooking up 56 million pizzas every year in Italy alone.

Food!   3

Oliver Twist

Oliver Twist is a young boy who is living in a kind of Victorian orphanage. The boys there are very badly treated and underfed. On this day, the boys decide that they want to be fed better …

1 Oliver Twist and his companions suffered the tortures of slow starvation for three months: at last they got so voracious and wild with hunger, that one boy, who was tall for his age, and hadn't been used to that sort of thing (for his father had kept a small cookshop), hinted darkly to his companions, that unless he had another basin of gruel, he was afraid he might some night happen to eat the boy who slept next him, who happened to be a weakly youth of tender age. He had a wild, hungry eye; and they implicitly believed him. A council was held; lots were cast who should walk up to the master after supper that evening, and ask for more; and it fell to Oliver Twist.

2 The evening arrived; the boys took their places. The master, in his cook's uniform, stationed himself at the copper; his pauper assistants ranged themselves behind him; the gruel was served out; and a long grace was said over the short commons. The gruel disappeared; the boys whispered to each other, and winked at Oliver; while his next neighbours nudged him. Child as he was, he was desperate with hunger, and reckless with misery. He rose from the table; and advancing to the master, basin and spoon in hand, said, somewhat alarmed at his own temerity:

3 "Please, sir, I want some more."

4 The master was a fat, healthy man; but he turned very pale. He gazed in stupefied astonishment on the small rebel for some seconds, and then clung for support to the copper. The assistants were paralysed with wonder; the boys with fear.

5 "What!" said the master at length, in a faint voice.

"Please, sir," replied Oliver, "I want some more."

6 The master aimed a blow at Oliver's head with the ladle; pinioned him in his arms; and shrieked aloud for the beadle.

7 The board were sitting in solemn conclave, when Mr. Bumble rushed into the room in great excitement, and addressing the gentleman in the high chair, said,

8 "Mr. Limbkins, I beg your pardon, sir! Oliver Twist has asked for more!"

9 There was a general start. Horror was depicted on every countenance.

10 "For more!" said Mr. Limbkins. "Compose yourself, Bumble, and answer me distinctly. Do I understand that he asked for more, after he had eaten the supper allotted by the dietary?"

11 "He did, sir," replied Bumble.

12 "That boy will be hung," said the gentleman in the white waistcoat. "I know that boy will be hung."

From *Oliver Twist* by Charles Dickens

Address: www.foodstandards.gov.uk › go

Live Home Page | Apple | Apple Support | Apple Store | .Mac | Mac OS X | Microsoft MacTopia »

Why is water good for you?

Why is it important to drink lots of water and how much should an adult drink each day?

1 Water is extremely important for our bodies to work properly. This is because water is responsible for moving nutrients around the body and most of the chemical reactions within our cells take place in water.

2 As your body works it produces waste products. Some of these waste products are toxic and the body gets rid of them through the kidneys in urine, which is mainly made up of water.

3 We also lose water by evaporation when we breathe and sweat. As the temperature rises and we do more activity, this increases the amount of water the body loses. To stay healthy, you need to replace the fluids that you lose.

4 In moderate climates, such as the UK, we should drink at least 6 to 8 cups/glasses of water (or other fluid) to prevent dehydration. In hotter climates your body will need more fluids.

5 Drinks that contain caffeine (such as tea, coffee and cola) can act as diuretics, which means they can make your body lose greater volumes of water than usual. So these drinks can lead to an increased need for water or other fluids that don't have a diuretic effect.

6 Drinks that contain sugar, such as fruit juice, some squashes and fizzy drinks, should also be drunk sparingly, because they can contribute to tooth decay. However, one glass of fruit juice can count towards the five portions of fruit and veg that we are recommended to eat each day.

With thanks to Food Standards Agency © Crown Copyright *foodstandards.gov.uk*

Sets

ABC

KEY STAGE 3
Levels 4–7

Instructions,
Answers and
Mark Scheme
Booklet

English

Instructions and
Answers

Instructions, Answers and Mark Scheme Booklet

This booklet provides advice on how to approach the SATs questions, as well as supplying the answers and the mark schemes for each of the Test Papers.

On page 27, there is a grid to record your marks in and a guide showing how your marks relate to levels.

Contents

Instructions on using the Practice Papers

These tests are similar to the tests you will take in May usually during your Year 9 year.

Each set comprises 5 tests and you must check how much time you have to complete each test. You should choose a period when you are not too tired and can work uninterrupted. You do not have to take the tests in one sitting. The questions have been written by experienced teachers and examination question writers, so important ideas are revisited.

As with the statutory tests, answers should be written in the booklet in the indicated spaces. At the end of one hour, the paper can be marked by referring to the answers and marks later in this booklet. After many of the answers, there is a useful tip from the examiners who have written these tests.

When you have taken the tests, they will be helpful to use to revise and prepare for the actual tests.

Tips for the Top

Make sure you have a suitable place to do the test and have a pen, pencil and rubber.

Try all of the questions and write your answers where you see the pencil.

e.g. _____

The number of marks is shown for each part of the question.

Remember to read the questions carefully.

Short answer questions

These questions test a range of different skills.
You will do well on this test paper by thinking about a number of things.

1   Organise your time. People who do well on this paper make sure that they spend an appropriate amount of time on each question. There are 32 marks for this paper, and you have one hour to write your answers, so you should be spending just under 2 minutes on each mark. Stick to this. If you get stuck, move on and come back to the missed questions at the end, if you have time.

2   Know what the questions require. The questions are testing different reading skills. Some require short answers, others need examples and some require a mixture. Obviously, the number of marks available and the amount of space for the answer gives some idea of how much to write, but you should also know what the different instruction words in the questions mean. Here is a range of commonly used instruction words used in this paper and what they require from you.

   "Give reasons" – explain – put things in your own words.
   "What does ... suggest?" – give your own personal opinion based on the way the word is used in the text.
   "Explain" – what it says! Use your own words.
   "Identify" – give an example, or a quotation.
   "What is the effect of ...?" – give your own personal opinion based on the way the word is used in the text.
   "Why is ...?" – explain – put things in your own words.

3   When filling in charts and boxes, don't put more answers than you are allowed. You will simply be given zero!

4   On the questions worth 5 marks, make sure you have a quotation and a comment on every bullet point. To get the top marks on the 5 marks questions, pick out individual words from your quotations and use those individual words to show exactly where you have got your ideas from.

The writing tasks

In school, all through KS3, you will have learnt about different styles of writing. The long and short writing tasks are testing to see if you know how to write in different styles. This means the following.

1   Revise what you have learnt in school about how to write in different styles, e.g. How do you write to:
    • imagine, explore, entertain?
    • argue, persuade, advise?
    • inform, explain, describe?
    • analyse, review, comment?

    If you revise what you have done on each of these writing types, then it will help you to get more marks for "Communication and effect" which carries the most marks on both the long and short tasks.

2   Plan your answer! If you want to get good marks for paragraphing and organisation, then it is essential to do a short plan first. It doesn't matter how you plan – you could brainstorm, mind map – do whatever suits your learning style. At the very least, decide what will happen in the beginning, middle and end of your writing. If you have time, decide what you are going to put in each paragraph.

3   Leave a short amount of time to proof-read what you have written. On the short task, make sure you check spelling, because you gain marks for "Spelling" on that task.

4   You don't have to worry about writing vast amounts, especially on the short answer task. The marker is looking for quality, not quantity.

The Shakespeare papers

Before you do a paper:
•   make sure that you understand what is happening in your scenes first
•   make sure that you know what the important quotations are in your scenes – what they are, what they mean and how you might explain them
•   know how your scenes relate to the rest of the play

In the SATs exam you should do the following:

1   Read the question carefully.

2   Write on the question paper – underline the key words in the question. Use these to identify what you have to include in your answer. A highlighter pen would be handy!

3   Use the words you have underlined in the question to help identify the quotations you are going to use from the extracts. Remember that the extracts given to you are only about half of the scenes you have studied. Again, a highlighter pen would be useful.

4   Plan your answer – make sure you cover all parts of the question required.

5   You can refer to other parts of the play, and probably will, but only do so in passing – there won't be time for you to answer the question properly if you focus on too much outside the set scenes. Use a quotation for every point you make. Pick words out of the quotations where possible,

because you will show more exactly where you have got your ideas from, which is essential to get Level 6 and Level 7.

6   To show your personal opinion on the language of the play, pick out words and use sentences like "the word … suggests to me … because …", "the words … imply that … because …". Frame your comments using sentence frames like these and you will be showing personal opinion and developing your ideas in depth, which should mean that you are commenting at least at Level 5 or above, depending on how thoroughly and sensibly you phrase your comments.

7   Make sure that you answer on both scenes. If you only answer on one scene, then the marker will mark your answer and drop your marks by one band in the mark scheme. This could mean you dropping a level on your overall Reading score, so manage your time carefully.

Set A Answers – "Food!" Reading Test Paper

Italy attempts to ban fake pizzas

1   It wants to crack down on chefs making bad copies of pizzas.
It wants to create strict rules about pizza making.
It wants a step-by-step guide to pizza making.
(1 mark for each different response, up to a maximum of 2 marks)

2   a) It suggests that they want to take extreme/firm/forceful action about the problem.   *(1 mark)*

    b) They suggest that the audience is one which accepts informal language,
i.e. children/young people.   *(1 mark)*

3   a)

Topic	Paragraph Number
Rules about the pizza	5
How the Margherita pizza got its name	9
A reaction from a top pizza chef	7
An introduction to the article	1

1 correct paragraph   *(0 marks)*
2 or 3 correct paragraphs   *(1 mark)*
4 correct paragraphs   *(2 marks)*

    b) It has these different kinds of paragraphs because:
the writer is trying to entertain as well as inform
it shows a variety of ways of convincing the reader of the truth of the story
(1 mark for either explanation)

4   Simple points made about the article, with limited awareness of how the writer tries to appeal to young people.   *(1 mark)*

Two examples of how the article is trying to appeal to young people, with some comment on how the text has this effect. Some awareness of effect is evident. Two of the three bullet points are addressed briefly.   *(2 marks)*

Shows some understanding of how facts and dates are used to make the article appeal to young people and an awareness of how the language and content affect the reader. Some references to the text are included to support ideas. The third bullet point is only briefly addressed.   *(3 marks)*

Some exploration of how the text tries to affect the reader through all three bullet points. A consistent attempt to comment on all three bullet points. References are used appropriately to support all ideas.   *(4 marks)*

A focused response which explores in detail, with close precise reference to the text, picking out individual words and phrases, how the article affects the reader. All three bullet points are addressed and a high level of awareness is shown by an understanding of different techniques that the writer has used.   *(5 marks)*

Oliver Twist

5 a) "suffered" or "tortures" (NOT "slow starvation" – the question says one word)   *(1 mark)*

  b) "suffered" – makes the reader think that they were in pain/had to put up with discomfort
  "tortures" – makes the reader think that their pain was terrible/really bad/inflicted by someone else/on purpose

  (1 mark for each valid response, linked to the answer to 5a)

6   It suggests that he is greedy.   *(1 mark)*

7 a) Features of Oliver Twist's character from this extract:
  He is brave (he accepts the challenge to ask for more/he accepts his beating)
  He is persistent (he asks for more twice)
  He doesn't care about his fate because he's so hungry
  He is surprised by his own bravery

  (1 mark for identifying any of the above)

  b) Features of the master's character:
  He is not used to being questioned or contradicted
  He is easily angered
  He is violent in nature   *(1 mark for identifying any of the above)*

8 a) It begins with long paragraphs and ends with shorter ones because:
  The writer switches from narrative description to dialogue
  The writer builds up the tension by describing the background first

  (1 mark for either explanation)

  b) It makes you feel sorry for Oliver because:
  It is the second time he has had to ask
  He is being well-mannered and reasonable and you would not expect anyone to refuse him

  (1 mark for either explanation)

9   The writer wants us to feel sorry for Oliver.   TRUE
  The writer is trying to criticise the way that boys like Oliver were treated by authority.   TRUE
  The writer is trying to give a factual historical account.   FALSE
  The writer is trying to entertain the reader.   TRUE

  1 correct   *(0 marks)*
  2 – 3 correct   *(1 mark)*
  4 correct   *(2 marks)*

Why is water good for you?

10 i It includes facts, e.g. "Water is extremely important for our bodies to work properly"
(1 mark – both reason and quotation needed)

   ii It gives reasons, e.g. " ... <u>because</u> water is responsible for moving nutrients around the body"/"<u>because</u> ... most of the chemical reactions within our cells take place in water"
(1 mark – reason and either valid quotation needed, but quotation must include the word "because" up to a maximum of 2 marks)

11

Word/Phrase	Effect on the reader	How it creates this effect on the reader
We also lose water by evaporation	makes the reader think that drinking water is important	because it suggests that we need to replace this water
To stay healthy	makes the reader think that drinking water is important	because it suggests that you will be ill if you don't drink it
We should drink at least 6 to 8 cups	makes the reader think that drinking water is important	because it suggests that there is a great need for it

(1 mark for a quotation accompanied by an appropriate explanation, up to a maximum of 2 marks)

12 a) It acts as a diuretic.
   You lose more water than normal.
   It makes you need more water than normal.   *(1 mark for any of these responses)*

   b) Brackets are used to <u>provide examples</u> of drinks that include caffeine.   *(1 mark)*

13 Simple points made about language or content, with limited awareness of how the writer tries to influence the reader.   *(1 mark)*

Two examples of how the language or content is making the article sound serious, with some comment on how the words influence the reader. Some awareness of effect is evident. Two of the three bullet points are addressed briefly.   *(2 marks)*

Shows some understanding of how the language and content make the article influence the reader. Some references to the text are included to support ideas. The third bullet point is only briefly addressed.   *(3 marks)*

Some exploration of how the language and content in the text try to influence the reader through all three bullet points. A consistent attempt to comment on all three bullet points. References are used appropriately to support all ideas.   *(4 marks)*

A focused response which explores in detail, with close precise reference to the text, picking out individual words and phrases, how the article affects the reader. All three bullet points are addressed and a high level of awareness is shown by an understanding of different techniques that the writer has used.   *(5 marks)*

Set B Answers – "Monsters" Reading Test Paper

Bigfoot of North America

1
- hairy
- ape-like
- biped
- 7 – 9 feet tall
- 600 – 900 pounds
- 14" by 8" footprint size
- 4 toes   *(1 mark for any of the above, up to a maximum of 2 marks)*

2   a) It suggests that:
- It might not be true
- There might have been earlier sightings that we don't know of
                                                              (1 mark for either of these responses)
    b) It suggests that:
- They're unusual
- They're not of a human or recognisable creature   *(1 mark for either of these responses)*

3   a)

Topic	Paragraph Number
A description of a captured Sasquatch	3
An introduction to what Bigfoot is	1
An explanation of what the captured Sasquatch might have been	4
The first sightings of a Sasquatch	2

1 correct paragraph   *(0 marks)*
2 or 3 correct paragraphs   *(1 mark)*
4 correct paragraphs   *(2 marks)*

    b) • To make the passage more convincing
       • To show that the Bigfoot has been sighted by a variety of people
                                                              (1 mark for either of these responses)

4   Simple points made about how Bigfoot is a fake, with limited awareness of how the writer makes the reader feel this.   *(1 mark)*

Two examples of how the article makes Bigfoot out to be a fake, with some comment on how the text has this effect. Some awareness of effect is evident. Two of the three bullet points are addressed briefly.   *(2 marks)*

Shows some understanding of how historical examples are used to make the account believable and an awareness of how the descriptions of Bigfoot affect the reader. Some references to the text are included to support ideas. The third bullet point is only briefly addressed.   *(3 marks)*

Some exploration of how the text tries to affect the reader through all three bullet points. A consistent attempt to comment on all three bullet points. References are used appropriately to support all ideas.   *(4 marks)*

A focused response which explores in detail, with close precise reference to the text, picking out individual words and phrases, how the article affects the reader. All three bullet points are addressed and a high level of awareness is shown by an understanding of different techniques that the writer has used. *(5 marks)*

Dracula

5 a) "for I did not know what to do" *(1 mark)*

   b) Because s/he has to read on to find out what the narrator does. *(1 mark)*

6 It suggests that:
   * They disapprove of the narrator
   * They don't like him *(1 mark for either appropriate response)*

7 a) "The old man motioned me in ... with a courtly gesture" *(1 mark)*

   b) Either of these quotations, or a summary of them, is acceptable:
   * The man is unusually strong/"grasped mine with a strength which made me wince"
   * The man does not seem alive or human/"more like the hand of a dead than a living man"
   (1 mark for an acceptable answer)

8 a) One mark for a difference that refers to both pairs of paragraphs – commenting on either paragraphs one and two or three and four alone gets no marks. The bit in brackets is not needed to get the mark – it is just to help you understand the answer.

   Valid comments about paragraphs one and two:
   * The writer uses lots of personal thoughts (to show us what he is thinking)
   * The writer uses a lot of self-questioning (to show he is confused)

   Valid comments about paragraphs three and four:
   * The writer describes the old man from the narrator's viewpoint (so that we see him through his eyes)
   * The writer describes the old man from the outside (so that we don't know what he's thinking, to make him more mysterious) *(1 mark)*

   b) It makes the story interesting because it:
   * Creates a sense of mystery
   * Makes us want to read on to find out who he is *(1 mark for either valid comment)*

9 The writer wants us to feel that the narrator is confident. *FALSE*
   The writer's aim is to entertain and interest the reader. *TRUE*
   The writer wants us to like the old man. *FALSE*
   The writer's aim is to build up tension in the reader. *TRUE*

   1 correct *(0 marks)*
   2 – 3 correct *(1 mark)*
   4 correct *(2 marks)*

The Loch Ness Monster

10 "The Loch Ness Monster is <u>supposedly</u> living in Scotland's Loch Ness"
"this <u>unidentified</u> animal"
"a <u>strange</u> aquatic creature"
(1 mark for identifying two of the above, up to a maximum of 2 marks for explanations of why these examples create a feeling of mystery – see the question)

11

Word/Phrase	Effect on the reader	How it creates this effect on the reader
convinced	makes the reader think that there might be some truth in the monster stories	because it suggests that the men had no doubts/believed what they saw
received several letters	makes the reader think that there might be some truth in the monster stories	because it suggests that the account made other people confess their experiences/come out with stories
claiming also to have seen	makes the reader think that there might be some truth in the monster stories	because it suggests that the account was backed up by other witnesses/other people had seen it

(1 mark for a quotation accompanied by an appropriate explanation, up to a maximum of 2 marks)

12 a) The writer uses the word "thorough" because:
   • It suggests that the scientists had done their job properly
   • It suggests that the entire loch has been surveyed   *(1 mark for either response)*

   b) It is in inverted commas because the writer is casting doubt on whether the monster deserves to be called a monster/whether it really is a monster.   *(1 mark for either response)*

13 Simple points made about language or content, with limited awareness of how the writer tries to make it sound serious.   *(1 mark)*

Two examples of how the language or content makes the article sound serious, with some comment on how the words affect the reader. Some awareness of effect is evident. Two of the three bullet points are addressed briefly.   *(2 marks)*

Shows some understanding of how the language and content make the article sound serious. Some references to the text are included to support ideas. The third bullet point is only briefly addressed.   *(3 marks)*

Some exploration of how the language and content in the text try to affect the reader through all three bullet points. A consistent attempt to comment on all three bullet points. References are used appropriately to support all ideas.   *(4 marks)*

A focused response which explores in detail, with close precise reference to the text, picking out individual words and phrases, how the article affects the reader. All three bullet points are addressed and a high level of awareness is shown by an understanding of different techniques that the writer has used.   *(5 marks)*

Set C Answers – "Down South" Reading Test Paper

Jean Lafitte

1 He established his own kingdom of Barataria.
He claimed to command more than 1000 men/provided them as troops for the Battle of New Orleans.
He engaged in the slave trade after it was banned.   *(1 mark for each up to a maximum of 2)*

2   a) He had a varied life/it contained a mixture of exciting/good/bad incidents.
                    (1 mark for an answer containing either of these explanations)

    b) His life has been exaggerated/his life is legendary
                    (1 mark for an answer containing either of these explanations)

3   a)

Topic	Paragraph Number
A summary of Jean Lafitte's main achievements	1
The end of Jean Lafitte's life	6
Two places that exist today, connected to Jean Lafitte	7
The history of a diary about Jean Lafitte	3
A place named after Jean Lafitte	8
Reasons why Jean Lafitte became famous	4

    1 correct paragraph   *(0 marks)*
    2 or 3 correct paragraphs   *(1 mark)*
    4 correct paragraphs   *(2 marks)*

    b) Because it's writing to inform/it's from a reference book/encyclopaedia.
                    (1 mark for an answer containing either of these explanations)

4   Simple points made about Jean Lafitte, with limited awareness of how the article tries to give the
    reader a fair view.   *(1 mark)*

    Two examples of how the article gives the reader a fair view, with some comment on how the
    text has this effect. Some awareness of effect is evident. Two of the three bullet points are
    addressed briefly.   *(2 marks)*

    Shows some understanding of how facts and dates are used to make the account believable and
    an awareness of how the descriptions of Jean Lafitte and his life affect the reader. Some
    references to the text are included to support ideas. The third bullet point is only briefly
    addressed.   *(3 marks)*

    Some exploration of how the text tries to affect the reader through all three bullet points.
    A consistent attempt to comment on all three bullet points. References are used appropriately to
    support all ideas.   *(4 marks)*

    A focused response which explores in detail, with close precise reference to the text, picking out
    individual words and phrases, how the article affects the reader. All three bullet points are
    addressed and a high level of awareness is shown by an understanding of different techniques
    that the writer has used.   *(5 marks)*

Arriving In New Orleans

5 a) coasted   *(1 mark)*

   b) That the roar is either:
   - hideous
   - frightening
   - suggesting that something is being killed or badly hurt
                                (1 mark for any of these acceptable responses)

6 They were eager to see their destination.   *(1 mark)*

7 It is smelly/"odour of mud"/"fetid stink of cesspools"/"smell of burning sugar".
   It is crowded/"teeming streets"/"noisy, thronged streets".
   It is derelict/"only charred timbers among rampant fireweed".
   The people are unfriendly/"The man did not answer, spat to his right".
                   (1 mark for any two of the above up to a maximum of 2 marks. Quotations or
                                            explanations are acceptable for a mark)

8 a) Getting off the boat.   *(1 mark)*

   b) There is an emphasis on bad things, e.g. the cow bogged in the mud, the smell.
      There are hints of fear – the "quivering ship", the "gruesome roar", the "red moon crawled".
            (1 mark for including one of the above reasons in the answer. No mark for an explanation
                                     not backed up with an example or quotation)

New Orleans

9 The writer wants us to be aware that New Orleans is a smelly place   TRUE
   The writer wants the reader to feel like the accordion maker   TRUE
   The aim of the writer is to scare the reader   FALSE
   The aim of the writer is to put people off visiting New Orleans   FALSE

   1 correct   *(0 marks)*
   2 – 3 correct   *(1 mark)*
   4 correct   *(2 marks)*

10 "seduces" – makes it sound like the place is chatting you up/enticing you/drawing you in like
    a lover.
    "sultry southern heat" – makes it sound sexy or steamy/alliteration "sultry southern" used
    to create a hot, steamy effect.
    "Caribbean colour" – it makes it seem lively and exotic/alliteration "Caribbean colour" used
    to create a lively effect.
      (1 mark for each explanation supported by a quotation from this list of acceptable responses up to
                                                    a maximum of 2 marks)

11

Word/Phrase	Effect on the reader	How it creates this effect on the reader
Enshrouding us in dreams	makes the reader think that New Orleans is exciting	because it suggests that it is a place of mystery/fantasy
sweet-tasting cocktails	makes the reader think that New Orleans is exciting	because it suggests that you can enjoy drinks that are better tasting/than in other places
laissez les bons temps rouler	makes the reader think that New Orleans is exciting	because it suggests that it is a party town/where people are just out to enjoy themselves
laced with voodoo potions	makes the reader think that New Orleans has a darker side	because it suggests that evil and black magic might affect you there without your knowledge
a well-earned reputation for excess and debauchery	makes the reader think that New Orleans has a darker side	because it suggests that people get out of control
The City That Care Forgot	makes the reader think that New Orleans has a darker side	because it suggests that the place is run down and abused

(1 mark for a quotation accompanied by an appropriate explanation, up to a maximum of 2 marks)

12 a) Because a checkerboard has a mix of black and white squares, just as New Orleans has a mix of contrasting neighbourhoods.   *(1 mark)*

   b) Because it's an explanation of the French word that comes before it.   *(1 mark)*

13 Simple points made about language, with limited awareness of how the article tries to make it sound an exciting place.   *(1 mark)*

   Two examples of how the language makes the article exciting, with some comment on how the words affect the reader. Some awareness of effect is evident. Two of the three bullet points are addressed briefly.   *(2 marks)*

   Shows some understanding of how the language makes New Orleans sound lively and mysterious. Some references to the text are included to support ideas. The third bullet point is only briefly addressed.   *(3 marks)*

   Some exploration of how the language in the text tries to affect the reader through all three bullet points. A consistent attempt to comment on all three bullet points. References are used appropriately to support all ideas.   *(4 marks)*

   A focused response which explores in detail, with close precise reference to the text, picking out individual words and phrases, how the article affects the reader. All three bullet points are addressed and a high level of awareness is shown by an understanding of different techniques that the writer has used.   *(5 marks)*

Writing Test Papers

The bands for writing give descriptions of the main features to look out for in your writing. Different bands have different amounts of marks in them.

For bands with three different marks, check the following.

- If your writing fits everything in that band, but shows no evidence of the bands above or below, give yourself the middle mark.

- If your writing fits everything in that band, but shows one piece of evidence of lower bands, give yourself the lower mark in the band.

- If your writing fits everything in that band, but shows one piece of evidence of higher bands, give yourself the higher mark in the band.

For bands with two marks, you need to do two of the things in the band to get the lower mark and everything in the band to get the higher mark.

For bands with one mark, you need to do everything in that band to get that mark.

It is important to look at the different marks you are getting in order to build up an accurate picture of the strengths and weaknesses of your writing – for example, you might get high marks on Composition and effect, but your spelling may be letting you down. If you know this, then you should focus on these areas when revising for your SATs.

Long Writing Task Papers – Mark Scheme

Section A: Sentence structure and punctuation

Band A1
Sentences and phrases are mostly linked with joining words like "and", "but" and "when".
Sentences are simple and may contain lots of repeated words and phrases.
Full stops, capital letters and exclamation marks are used to punctuate sentences, mostly accurately.

(0 marks)

Band A2
Sentences are varied, and more complex joining words like "who" and "which" are used.
Words like "if" and "because" are used to help give reasons and for emphasising ideas.
Commas are used quite accurately within sentences.

(1 or 2 marks)

Band A3
Simple and more complex sentences are used – long sentences and short sentences are used successfully.
Suggestions are given, by using words like "can" or "would".
A variety of punctuation is used with accuracy.
Different types of sentences, e.g. commands, questions or exclamations, are used in order to create more interesting effects.

(3 or 4 marks)

Band A4
The writer begins sentences more skilfully, with words like "usually", "hopefully" etc. or by being impersonal, e.g. "Some people believe that ...".
A range of punctuation is used and this is sometimes done for deliberate effect, e.g. brackets are used to put in asides and thoughts.

(5 or 6 marks)

Band A5
Sentences are varied, depending on the effect that the writer wishes to create.
Simple sentences might be used, but to create effects, e.g. shock or surprise.
Punctuation is used skilfully in order to make the reader speed up and slow down and to make the meaning of the writing perfectly clear.   *(7 marks)*

Band A6
A wide range of sentence types is used with skill, accuracy and thought to control the writing.
There might be some non-standard sentences, but used for deliberate effect.
There is a very wide range of different types of punctuation used, in order to create a number of different effects.   *(8 marks)*

Section B: Text structure and organisation

This section focuses on how overall meaning and effect is put across through the way that the writing is organised and planned.

Band B1
Ideas are mainly linked because they happen to be on the same topic.
Points might be put in a list, but not necessarily in any sort of order of importance.
Paragraphs might be used to show some of the obvious different topics in the writing.   *(0 marks)*

Band B2
Paragraphs usually start with the main topic in the first sentence.
Paragraphs contain examples.
The writing has some brief opening and closing comments, but they will be fairly brief and undeveloped.   *(1 or 2 marks)*

Band B3
Paragraphs are written in a logical order.
The introduction and conclusion are clear.
Paragraphs of different lengths are used, e.g. short paragraphs might take the form of a persuasive question.   *(3 or 4 marks)*

Band B4
Detailed content is well handled within and between paragraphs.
Some phrases like "On the other hand" or "In addition to this" etc. are used to link the paragraphs.
The introduction and conclusion to the letter are developed and help to make it more persuasive.
  (5 or 6 marks)

Band B5
Paragraphs are varied in length to suit the different ideas being discussed.
Paragraphs are linked with a variety of words and phrases.
Paragraphs are ordered in such a way that the writer might have used them to highlight contrasts, or to be ironic.   *(7 marks)*

Band B6
The whole piece of writing is organised, shaped and controlled to achieve a range of effects, or to get the reader thinking in a certain way.
Within paragraphs, the writer has used a wide range of links that are precisely and carefully chosen.
  (8 marks)

Section C: Composition and effect

This section focuses on the overall impact of the writing and the effect it has on the reader.

Band C1
The writing shows some awareness of the reader.
There is some relevant content. *(0 marks)*

Band C2
The writing is generally lively and attempts to interest the reader.
The content of the writing shows that the writer recognises its purpose.
Some reasons are given for the ideas and opinions, but perhaps not that many. *(1, 2 or 3 marks)*

Band C3
The writing is detailed and gives clear reasons for the opinions and viewpoints expressed.
The writing engages the reader's interest.
The writing gives a range of relevant ideas and the writer's viewpoint is clear. *(4, 5 or 6 marks)*

Band C4
The piece is well written because it uses a range of techniques such as repetition, humour and a consideration of the reader's needs in order to persuade.
The writer's view is consistent. *(7, 8 or 9 marks)*

Band C5
The tone and content of the writing are appropriate and well judged.
The writing deliberately interacts with the reader.
Content is relevant throughout and is used to support the ideas. *(10, 11 or 12 marks)*

Band C6
The writing has been done skilfully and the writer is totally in control of the writing type.
The viewpoint of the writer has been maintained throughout.
There is a strong individual style, created by a range of methods. *(13 or 14 marks)*

Short Writing Task Papers – Mark Scheme

Section D: Sentence structure, punctuation and paragraph organisation

This section focuses on how you choose to organise your writing and how this contributes to its overall effect.

Band D1
Sentences are fairly simple.
Sentences are linked by simple joining words like "and" or "then".
Full stops and capital letters are used with accuracy.
Paragraphs are used to separate the more obvious different topics given in the task.   *(0 marks)*

Band D2
Sentences are varied and use linking words like "who" or "which".
The writing is written in the same tense throughout.
Words like "he", "she", "it," "they" and other pronouns are generally used correctly.
Paragraphs are mainly put into a logical order, as is the detail within them.   *(1 or 2 marks)*

Band D3
A variety of longer sentences is used. This includes those sentences that have been built up from joining simpler ones together to make longer ones and sentences where the word order has been successfully re-arranged for effect.
Words like "completely", "partly" and others which help to make meaning more precise, are used.
Words like "he", "she", "it", "they" and other pronouns are used correctly.
Tenses are used correctly.
Paragraphs are used for appropriate reasons and are put into a logical order.
The detail in them is put into a logical order.   *(3 or 4 marks)*

Band D4
Sentences are written in a variety of ways to achieve interesting effects that suit the purpose of the writing.
A range of punctuation is used – sometimes to create effects!
Paragraphs are of different lengths and the information in them is organised cleverly to suit what is being written about.   *(5 marks)*

Band D5
There is a wide range of sentence structures that use a sophisticated range of verbs and tenses.
Within paragraphs, the writer has used a wide range of links that are precisely and carefully chosen.
There is a very wide range of punctuation used, in order to make meaning clear and create a range of effects.   *(6 marks)*

Section E: Composition and effect

This section is to do with the overall impact of your writing and how well it fits the audience you are writing for.

Band E1
The writing shows some awareness of the reader.
Simple techniques, like repetition, are used.
Content is relevant to the question, but might well be unevenly used. *(0 marks)*

Band E2
The writing tries to interest the reader.
Some techniques, e.g. use of adjectives, are used to help writing, but they might not be
very imaginative. *(1, 2 or 3 marks)*

Band E3
The writer interests the reader.
The writer is clearly aware of what type of writing he/she is doing and for whom.
The tone of the writing is consistent throughout. *(4, 5 or 6 marks)*

Band E4
The writing is well written and convincing throughout.
The writer really engages the reader's interest.
There is a very good range of well-chosen details.
The viewpoint of the writer is consistent throughout. *(7, 8 or 9 marks)*

Band E5
The writing has been done skilfully and the writer is totally in control of the writing type.
The viewpoint of the writer has been maintained throughout.
There is a strong individual style, created by a range of methods. *(10 marks)*

Section F: Spelling

This section focuses on accuracy in spelling. Choose the section that best fits the writing.

Band F1
Simple words and those with more than one or two syllables are generally accurate. *(1 mark)*

Band F2
More complicated words that fit to regular patterns and rules are generally accurate. *(2 marks)*

Band F3
Most spelling, including irregular words, is accurate. *(3 marks)*

Band F4
Virtually all spelling, including complex words that don't fit to regular rules or patterns, is correct.
(4 marks)

Shakespeare Test Papers – Mark Scheme

The Tempest mark scheme

The mark bands apply to all three Tempest questions.

Find the band that best fits your answer and for every bullet point in that band that you achieve, give yourself one mark within that band. e.g. if you think you are in Band 4 and you have done two of the bullet points, then you should give yourself 11.

Band 1
A few simple facts and opinions about these extracts.
There may be some misunderstandings.
Parts of the extracts are retold or copied and answers may be only partly relevant.   *(1, 2 or 3 marks)*

Band 2
Contains a little explanation, showing some awareness of the needs of the question.
Comments are relevant but are mostly about the plot.
Some broad references to how the characters speak   *(4, 5 or 6 marks)*

Band 3
Some general understanding of the question, although some points might not be developed.
Some comments on the language that the characters use.
Some points backed up with reference to the text.   *(7, 8 or 9 marks)*

Band 4
Some discussion of how the extracts relate to the question, even though all the ideas might not be of equal quality.
Awareness of the characters' use of language and its effects
Most points backed up with references to the text.   *(10, 11 or 12 marks)*

Band 5
Clear focus on how the extracts relate to the question
Good consistent comments on the characters' language and its effects
Well-chosen quotations linked together to present an overall argument.   *(13, 14 or 15 marks)*

Band 6
Every quotation is analysed in depth with relation to the question.
Every quotation is commented on in terms of the language that the characters use.
Individual words are picked out of quotations and linked into the overall argument.   *(16, 17 or 18 marks)*

Useful quotations for the Tempest Set A

Act 1 Scene 2
The fringèd curtains of thine eye advance,
And say what thou see'st yond.
    This shows how Prospero controls his daughter.

    It goes on, I see,
As my soul prompts it.
    This shows how Prospero is pleased by events because he wants to twist them for his own purposes.

At the first sight
They have changed eyes. Delicate Ariel,
I'll set thee free for this.
    This shows how he is a plotter and a schemer.

But this swift business
I must uneasy make, lest too light winning
Make the prize light.
    This shows how he enjoys plotting and scheming and making others suffer.

Thou dost here usurp
The name thou ow'st not – and hast put thyself
Upon this island as a spy, to win it
From me, the lord on't.
    This shows how he acts as a catalyst or trigger to later plot developments.

Act 3 Scene 1
Fair encounter
Of two most rare affections! Heavens rain grace
On that which breeds between 'em!
    This shows that he is continuing to control and scheme.

So glad of this as they I cannot be,
Who are surprised with all
    This shows that he is pleased for his own selfish ends.

I'll to my book –
For yet, ere supper-time, must I perform
Much business appertaining.
    This shows how he likes plotting for plotting's sake.

Useful quotations for the Tempest Set B

Act 1 Scene 2
What is't? A spirit?
    This shows Miranda's innocence.

I might call him
A thing divine, for nothing natural
I ever saw so noble.
    This shows us how she has fallen in love at first sight.

Why speaks my father so ungently? This
Is the third man that e'er I saw – the first
That e'er I sighed for.
    This again shows her naive nature, but towards her father's intentions.

There's nothing ill can dwell in such a temple.
If the ill spirit have so fair a house,
    This shows how she judges on appearance.

Act 3 Scene 1

Alas now, pray you
Work not so hard!
>   This demonstrates her concern for Ferdinand.

If you'll sit down.
I'll bear your logs the while.
>   This shows that she is prepared to put others before herself.

Poor worm, thou art infected!
This visitation shows it.
>   This shows that her love for Ferdinand is obvious to others.

How features are abroad,
I am skilless of
>   Miranda herself admits her lack of experience and awareness.

Useful quotations for the Tempest Set C

Act 1 Scene 2

...thou might'st call him
A goodly person.
>   The first comment made about Ferdinand makes the audience realise that he has virtue.

Most sure the goddess
On whom these airs attend!
>   The audience see he is instantly attracted to Miranda

O, you wonder! –
If you be maid or no?
>   Ferdinand is so overcome by Miranda, that he can't believe she is human.

O, if a virgin,
And your affection not gone forth, I'll make you
The Queen of Naples!
>   Ferdinand wants to prove the strength of his feelings for Miranda by making big promises.

Act 3 Scene 1

This my mean task
Would be as heavy to me as odious, but
The mistress which I serve quickens what's dead,
And makes my labours pleasures.
>   He is only doing this work because the thought of Miranda is spurring him on.

O most dear mistress,
The sun will set before I shall discharge
What I must strive to do.
>   Ferdinand dislikes the task he has been given because it is so long and tiresome.

No, precious creature.
I had rather crack my sinews, break my back,
Than you should such dishonour undergo,
>   This shows how, despite all his discomfort, he puts Miranda before himself.

What is your name?

This shows how strongly Ferdinand must feel, because he has fallen in love with her without knowing her name or who she is.

> *For several virtues*
> *Have I liked several women – never any*
> *With so full soul, but some defect in her*
> *Did quarrel with the noblest grace she owed,*

Ferdinand admits that he has found imperfections in all the women he has previously met, suggesting that he is hard to please.

> *But you – o you,*
> *So perfect and so peerless*

This shows how Ferdinand believes that Miranda is the person for him – because of her perfection.

Romeo and Juliet mark scheme

The mark bands apply to all three Romeo and Juliet questions.

Find the band that best fits your answer and for every bullet point in that band that you achieve, give yourself one mark within that band. e.g if you think you are in Band 4 and you have done two of the bullet points, then you should give yourself 11.

Band 1
A few simple facts and opinions about these extracts.
There may be some misunderstandings.
Parts of the extracts are retold or copied and answers may be only partly relevant.   *(1, 2 or 3 marks)*

Band 2
Contains a little explanation, showing some awareness of the needs of the question.
Comments are relevant but are mostly about the plot.
Some broad references to how the characters speak   *(4, 5 or 6 marks)*

Band 3
Some general understanding of the question, although some points might not be developed.
Some comments on the language that the characters use.
Some points backed up with reference to the text.   *(7, 8 or 9 marks)*

Band 4
Some discussion of how the extracts relate to the question, even though all the ideas might not be of equal quality.
Awareness of the characters' use of language and its effects
Most points backed up with references to the text.   *(10, 11 or 12 marks)*

Band 5
Clear focus on how the extracts relate to the question
Good consistent comments on the characters' language and its effect on the audience
Well-chosen quotations linked together to present an overall argument.   *(13, 14 or 15 marks)*

Band 6
Every quotation is analysed in depth with relation to the question and there is an evaluation.
Every quotation is commented on in terms of the language that the characters use.
Individual words are picked out of quotations and linked into the overall argument.   *(16, 17 or 18 marks)*

Useful quotations for Romeo and Juliet Set A

Act 1 Scene 1
Out of her favour where I am in love.
   Romeo is depressed about his love for Rosaline being unrequited.

O brawling love, O loving hate,
O anything of nothing first create!
O heavy lightness, serious vanity,
Misshapen chaos of well-seeming forms!
   The use of oxymorons shows how Romeo is confused.

Love is a smoke made with the fume of sighs:
   Romeo is acting out what he thinks a lover should do, but he has, as yet, no experience himself.

In sadness, cousin, I do love a woman.
    Romeo shows he still has a sense of humour, when with people he likes, like his cousin, Benvolio.

She will not stay the siege of loving terms,
Nor bide th' encounter of assailing eyes,
    Romeo is frustrated that Rosaline does not love him in return.

Farewell. Thou canst not teach me to forget.
    Romeo is stubborn.

Act 2 Scene 2
Her eye discourses. I will answer it.
– I am too bold.
    Romeo is anxious not to mess things up with Juliet.

O that I were a glove upon that hand,
That I might touch that cheek!
    Romeo displays the typically obsessive and exaggerated behaviour of a lover.

O speak again, bright angel! – For thou art
As glorious to this night, being o'er my head,
As is a wingèd messenger of heaven
    Romeo uses the clichéd language of love because he knows no better.

Call me but love, and I'll be new-baptized.
Henceforth, I never will be Romeo.
    Romeo makes strong promises, showing his innocence and strength of feeling.

Useful quotations for Romeo and Juliet Set B

Act 1 Scene 1
So early walking did I see your son.
Towards him I made, but he was ware of me,
And stole into the covert of the wood.
    This shows the secretive behaviour of lovers.

Many a morning hath he there been seen,
With tears augmenting the fresh morning's dew,
    Romeo is acting like a typical courtly lover of the time by showing his emotions to "prove" he is in love.

And makes himself an artificial night.
Black and portentous must this humour prove,
    Romeo's behaviour is stereotypical of a depressed lover.

Could we but learn from whence his sorrows grow,
We would as willingly give cure as know.
    This shows how others get concerned when someone is supposedly in love.

ROMEO
Dost thou not laugh?
BENVOLIO
No, coz, I rather weep.
    This shows how lovers get things out of proportion and lose their sense of emotional balance.

Act 2 Scene 2

What man art thou, that thus bescreened in night
So stumblest on my counsel?
    This shows how a lover's behaviour can seem shocking and unsettling.

JULIET
Art thou Romeo, and a Montague?
ROMEO
Neither, fair maid, if either thee dislike.
    This shows how lovers make extreme promises that they can't necessarily keep.

For stony limits cannot hold love out –
    This shows how love gives a person strength.

Alack, there lies more peril in thine eye
Than twenty of their swords.
    This shows how love makes a person reckless.

Useful quotations for Romeo and Juliet Set C

Act 1 Scene 1

O where is Romeo? Saw you him today?
Right glad I am he was not at this fray.
    This shows how Romeo's mother is concerned for his physical well-being.

Could we but learn from whence his sorrows grow,
We would as willingly give cure as know.
    This shows that Romeo's parents are concerned about his emotional well-being.

BENVOLIO
It was. What sadness lengthens Romeo's hours?
ROMEO
Not having that which, having, makes them short.
BENVOLIO
In love?
ROMEO
Out –
BENVOLIO
Of love?
ROMEO
Out of her favour where I am in love.
    These short, sensitive questions show Benvolio's concern for his cousin.

Act 2 Scene 2

What man art thou, that thus bescreened in night
So stumblest on my counsel?
    This shows how Juliet is, at first, shocked by Romeo's behaviour – until she realises who it is.

I would not for the world they saw thee here.
    This shows how quickly Juliet reveals the strength of her feelings for Romeo.

But farewell compliment!
Dost thou love me? I know thou wilt say 'Ay' –
And I will take thy word. Yet if thou swear'st
Thou mayst prove false. At lovers' perjuries
They say Jove laughs.

Juliet shows here that she thinks that she is rushing into relationship with Romeo, but can't stop herself.

O swear not by the moon, th' inconstant moon,
That monthly changes in her circled orb,
Lest that thy love prove likewise variable.

Juliet is worried that Romeo will prove to be fickle in his feelings.

My bounty is as boundless as the sea,
My love as deep. The more I give to thee,
The more I have, for both are infinite.

Juliet shows how quickly she has completely fallen for Romeo.

Marking the Tests and Assessing Levels

Enter your scores in the grid below and then work out your level using the mark ranges at the bottom of the page.

To work out your Reading level, add your scores for the Reading Test Paper short answer questions and the Shakespeare Test Paper. Make a note of your score in the table below and use the chart at the bottom of the page to find your level.

To work out your Writing level, add your scores for the short and long writing tasks. Make a note of your score in the table below and use the chart at the bottom of the page to find your level.

To find your overall level, add together your total Reading and Writing scores. Make a note of your score in the table below and use the chart at the bottom of the page to find your level.

Paper	Set A	Set B	Set C
Reading Test Paper – short answer questions			
Shakespeare Test Paper			
Reading total			
Reading level			
Short writing task			
Long writing task			
Writing total			
Writing level			

To find your Reading, Writing and Overall levels, use the charts below.

Level	Reading mark range	Writing mark range	Overall
No level	Below 8	Below 5	0 – 10
3	8 – 10	5 – 10	11 – 15
4	11 – 16	11 – 12	16 – 30
5	17 – 26	13 – 22	31 – 50
6	27 – 33	23 – 31	51 – 65
7	34 – 50	32 – 50	66 – 100

Remember that the Level obtained in these tests can be different from the levels obtained in the SATs tests. However, attempting these tests and getting some explanation where you went wrong will help you to achieve your best result.

How well have you done in these tests?
The results show whether or not you have reached the expected National Curriculum level for your age.

	Aged 7	Aged 11	Aged 14
Level 1	Below average		
Level 2 Level 2a Level 2b Level 2c	At level expected	Below average	
Level 3	Excellent	Below average	Below average
Level 4	Exceptional	At level expected	Below average
Level 5		Excellent	At level expected
Level 6		Exceptional	At level expected
Level 7			Excellent
Level 8			Exceptional

What do the levels mean?
When your English papers are marked, the correct marks are collated to give you an overall score. This score is then matched to a National Curriculum level.

It is expected that the majority of 14 year olds will achieve Level 5/6 by the end of Year 9. However, for some, achieving Level 7 is a real success for that particular individual. A pupil achieving Level 8 is working at a high level. A pupil who passes GCSE at grade C has achieved level 7.

67.KS3.E.A.28/1(09)

Sets
ABC

KEY STAGE 3
English
Levels 4–7

Instructions and
Level Assessment
Supplement

English

Instructions and Level
Assessment Supplement

Instructions and Level Assessment Supplement

Using this Pack for Self-Assessment

This pack of test papers provides a means of parental- or self-assessment that can be easily carried out at home. On completing each set of papers you will be able to evaluate an approximate level of attainment (using the table in this document), highlight opportunities for further study and skills practice that will aid improvement, and record results to track progress.

The instructions and guidelines within this supplement replace those that appear at the beginning and end of the 'Instructions, Answers and Mark Scheme Booklet' enclosed in the pack and provide guidance on how to use the test papers for self-assessment purposes.

You should still use the 'Instructions, Answers and Mark Scheme Booklet' to mark the test papers. The examiner's tips included with the answers provide helpful hints on how to remember key facts and improve results, but please ignore any references to SATs questions and / or papers. These references are no longer valid, but do not affect the assessment tests.

About the Assessment Test Papers

This pack contains three sets of assessment papers. The questions have been written by experienced teachers and are based on the programme of study for Key Stage 3.

Sets A, B and C each provide one complete assessment and comprises...
- 1 x Reading Booklet
- 1 x Reading Test Paper (1 hour 15 minutes)
- 1 x Writing Test Paper (1 hour 15 minutes)
- 3 x Shakespeare Test Papers (45 minutes)*

*Only complete the Shakespeare Test Paper that is relevant to the play you are studying.

The three tests can be taken at different times, but try to complete a set all within the same week. Take the tests at a time when you can work uninterrupted and do not feel too tired.

You should complete Sets A, B and C at intervals throughout Key Stage 3. Make sure you leave a reasonable amount of time between each assessment – it is unrealistic to expect to see an improvement in just a few weeks! You will feel much more motivated if you wait for a while, because your progress will be more obvious.

If you want to re-use the test papers, you can write in pencil and then rub out your answers. But don't repeat the same test paper too soon; otherwise you will remember the questions and your results will not be an accurate reflection of your abilities.

Before you start...
- find a suitable place to complete the tests – somewhere quiet, where you won't be disturbed
- make sure you have a pen, pencil, ruler, rubber and a clock or watch to time yourself
- turn off your mobile phone
- read the instructions on the front of the test paper and on pages 2–3 of the 'Instructions, Answers and Mark Scheme Booklet' carefully.

When completing the test papers
- try to answer all of the questions and make sure you read them carefully
- write your answers for the Reading Test in the spaces provided on the test paper
- write your answers for the Writing Test and Shakespeare Test on lined paper
- keep an eye on the time – if you spend longer than the allocated time on the paper your results will not accurately reflect your abilities.

When you've finished...
- use the answers and marks provided in the 'Instructions, Answers and Mark Scheme Booklet' to mark the test paper
- read the top tips on how to improve your performance and remember the key points
- add up the total number of marks.

Using Your Marks to Assess Levels

Record your test marks in the progress grid below:

	Set A Week beginning: __/__/__	Set B Week beginning: __/__/__	Set C Week beginning: __/__/__
Reading Test			
Shakespeare Test			
Reading Total			
Reading Level			
Writing Test – Short Task			
Writing Test – Long Task			
Writing Total			
Writing Level			

When you have completed all three tests in a set...
* add the marks for the Reading Test and Shakespeare Test together to give a total mark out of 50 for Reading
* add the marks for the Writing Test Short Task and Long Task together to give a total mark out of 50 for Writing.

The table below will give you an indication of your Reading, Writing and Overall levels based on your marks:

Level	Reading mark range	Writing mark range	Overall
No level	0–7	0–4	0–10
3	8–10	5–10	11–15
4	11–16	11–12	16–30
5	17–26	13–22	31–50
6	27–33	23–31	51–65
7	34–50	32–50	66–100

Remember that the level obtained in these tests may be different from the level that your teacher reports you are working at. This is because they can only test a limited range of skills and knowledge. Your teacher will have a better idea of your overall performance. However, these tests will help you to identify areas of weakness that you can improve upon with a bit of hard work and extra study, which will help you to get a better mark on your next assessment test and progress at school.

Improving Your Results and Making Progress

Go back through your test papers and make a note of all the questions that you got wrong. This will help you to identify skills that require further practice.

If you want to improve your understanding and make progress, you need to be proactive! Use Study Guides and Workbooks for home study – they include lots of practice questions, which test your knowledge, reinforce what you have learned and help to develop essential skills.

With a little bit of time and effort, when you take the next set of tests in the pack you will achieve a higher mark. Remember to record the date alongside your marks in the grid above. This will allow you to track your progress over time and will help to build your confidence and a sense of achievement.

What Do Levels Mean?

Attainment Levels are used to measure your progress through Key Stages 1, 2 and 3.
They are concerned with your knowledge, skills and understanding of a subject.

There are 8 levels and they each have a description, which sets out the skills, knowledge and understanding that you are expected to demonstrate at that level. The descriptions for Levels 1 to 8 get increasingly difficult.

Although there are 8 levels, at Key Stage 3 you are generally expected to work between Levels 3 and 7, where Level 7 represents excellent knowledge, skills and understanding.

The table below shows the expected National Curriculum levels for 7, 11 and 14 year olds.

	Aged 7	Aged 11	Aged 14
Level 1	Below average		
Level 2 Level 2a Level 2b Level 2c	At level expected	Below average	
Level 3	Excellent	Below average	Below average
Level 4	Exceptional	At level expected	Below average
Level 5		Excellent	At level expected
Level 6		Exceptional	At level expected
Level 7			Excellent
Level 8			Exceptional

As you can see, it is expected that a majority of 14 year olds will achieve Level 5 or 6 by the end of Year 9. If you achieve Level 7, it is a real success. A 14 year old who achieves Level 8 is working at an exceptionally high level. For comparison, a student who gains a GCSE grade C has achieved Level 7.

Your teacher will carry out regular assessments to ensure that you are working at an appropriate level and progressing at the expected rate. The test papers in this pack support this process. Providing you follow the instructions provided and address any potential problems that the tests highlight, they will help to ensure you are always working to the best of your abilities.